Dear Parents,

Are you aware that students can lose up to 25% of their reading and math skills during the summer vacation break away from academics*? While the freedom away from school during the summer break can be a wonderful time in your child's life, the reality is children will experience summer learning loss if they don't practice the skills they developed during the school year. That is why we created Summer Vacation®, a valuable investment in your child's future. Summer Vacation is a fun, entertaining educational program to help your child review skills learned during the previous school year and prepare them for the challenges of the next.

This 2nd grade activity workbook has been thoroughly reviewed and recommended by an esteemed panel of teachers. It is packed with fun, skills-based activities for every day of the summer. Some of the activities in this book include:

- New chapter story with fun reading comprehension activities
- New progressive project – "Make a Constellation Projector"
- New fun stickers to track progress
- Counting coins up to $1.00
- Identification of simple fractions
- Use of math symbols and place value up to 100s column
- Identification of parts of speech
- Drawing, arts and crafts activities
- Simple telling time exercises

We suggest that you work with your child as necessary to complete the activities in this workbook. It may be beneficial to pick a certain time each day to work on the activities. This consistency will help make participation a habit, and will provide some quality time that will ultimately assist with your child's educational development.

We hope you and your child enjoy Summer Vacation®!

*Source: Harris Cooper, professor and chairman of the psychology department at the University of Missouri at Columbia.

Summer Vacation® Teacher Review Panel

Our panel of distinguished educators was instrumental in ensuring that the Summer Vacation® program offers your child maximum educational benefit. This panel provided key ideas and feedback on all aspects of our workbook series. We welcome your feedback.

Please contact us at:
Attn: Summer Vacation, Entertainment Publications, 2125 Butterfield Road, Troy, Michigan 48084
or e-mail us at
summervacation@entertainment.com.

Cathy Cerveny, Baltimore, MD
Maryland Teacher of the Year, 1996
Fifth-grade teacher; Integrated
Language Arts curriculum writer
Served on Maryland's Professional
Standards and Teacher Education Board

Norma Jackson, Keller, TX
Texas Teacher of the Year, 1999
On special assignment as District Writing
Specialist for grades K–5
Second-grade teacher
Summer Activity Writing Specialist

Becky Miller, Mason, OH
Gifted Coordinator for Mason City Schools
Taught elementary grades 3 and 4
Adjunct Professor at
Xavier University

Laurie Sybert, Lake Ozark, MO
Missouri Teacher of the Year, 1999
Second-grade teacher
Elementary Science coordinator
Fulbright Teacher Scholar

Jenlane Gee Matt, Modesto, CA
California Teacher of the Year, 1988
National Teacher of the Year finalist, 1989
Third-grade teacher

Gemma Hoskins, Bel Air, MD
Maryland Teacher of the Year, 1992
Technology Coordinator for school
Former fifth-grade teacher and
elementary teacher specialist

Charles Mercer, Washington, DC
District of Columbia Teacher of the Year, 1999
Worked at NASA's Education Program Office
Elementary Science resource
teacher, PK–6

Denise Johnson, New York, NY
Teacher Center Specialist in Manhattan
Previously taught grades 4–8
Instructor at Brooklyn College

**Richard Scott Griffin,
Mount Holly, NC**
North Carolina Teacher of the Year, 199●
Teaches grades 4-6—all subject areas
Served as Teacher Advisor to State Boar●
of Education

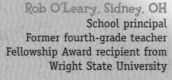

Rob O'Leary, Sidney, OH
School principal
Former fourth-grade teacher
Fellowship Award recipient from
Wright State University

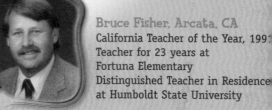

Bruce Fisher, Arcata, CA
California Teacher of the Year, 199●
Teacher for 23 years at
Fortuna Elementary
Distinguished Teacher in Residence
at Humboldt State University

Getting Ready for Second Grade

In the first grade, your child took his or her first steps toward becoming an independent reader and writer. Your first-grade graduate may be able to:

- read at least 100 words.
- locate the main idea in stories.
- remember the sequence of events in stories.
- print words legibly.
- capitalize the first word in a sentence.
- use a period or a question mark at the end of a sentence.
- recognize the singular and plural forms of nouns.
- use phonetic skills to "sound out" words.
- correctly spell some simple words.
- count to 100 in increments of 1, 2, 5, and 10.
- write numerals to 100.
- add and subtract numbers up to 10.
- understand the place value for two-digit numbers.

Grade 2 Skills

Second grade is a time for children to become increasingly proficient in their basic skills. They will learn to add and subtract faster, compose more complex sentences, and increase their reading and speaking vocabularies. By the end of second grade, your child may be able to:

- apply more complex phonetic reading skills.
- read more than 200 commonly used words.
- use correct punctuation when writing sentences.
- correctly spell some complex words.
- write longer stories on a specific theme or idea.
- recognize nouns and verbs in sentences.
- identify synonyms and antonyms.
- write legibly in cursive.
- understand place value for three-digit numbers.
- add and subtract three-digit numbers.
- tell time down to five-minute intervals.
- understand the value of pennies, nickels, dimes, quarters, half-dollars, and dollars.

How You Can Help

You can help prepare your child for second grade by making this Summer Vacation® workbook a regular part of your daily routine. Read the stories together, and help your child with the written activities and the constellation projector. The Summer Vacation book is designed to help your child retain the skills that he or she developed in first grade and to prepare him or her for the challenges of second grade.

Chapter 1: Follow the Tracks

Ask an adult to help you read this story.

Hornsby is a big, clever rhinoceros. Fuzzbuzz is a tiny, helpful dragonfly. They both live in the jungle. Hornsby and Fuzzbuzz are best friends because they both love adventures.

One summer day Hornsby said, "Let's go swimming."

"Good idea," said Fuzzbuzz.

They walked down the path to the river.

Hornsby stopped. "Look at these strange paw prints," he said.

Activity 1

Skill: Sentence Sequence

Put the words in order to make a complete sentence. It will tell something that happened in the story.

1 see   2 Hornsby   6 prints   4 Fuzzbuzz   5 paw   3 and

Fuzzbuzz said, "They are very small. I think it is a baby animal."

"But there is only one set of prints," said Hornsby. "Why would a baby be all alone?"

"Maybe the baby is in trouble," said Fuzzbuzz.

"Let's follow the tracks," said Hornsby. "Maybe we can help."

Activity 2
Skill: Word Meaning

Circle the picture that shows something *small*.

TUESDAY

Matching

Draw lines to connect the math equation to the correct answer.

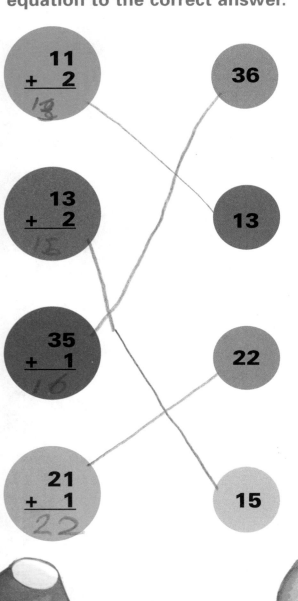

11
+ 2
13

13
+ 2
15

35
+ 1
16

21
+ 1
22

36

13

22

15

Learn to Draw

Draw the object below by copying the drawings in each numbered step on a piece of paper.

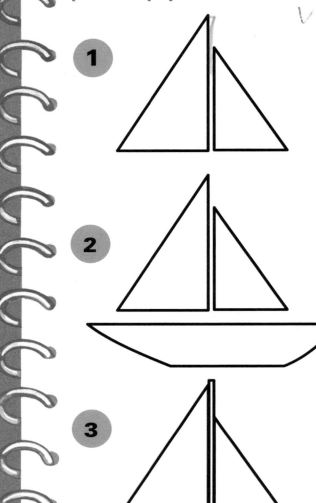

1

2

3

4

Can You Find?

Circle the characters hidden in the picture.

Fuzzbuzz

Birdie

Hornsby

WEDNESDAY

Pretzel Owl

Adult supervision is recommended.

Materials:

small twisted pretzel

small stick pretzel

walnut shell

o-shaped cereal

white glue

small piece of loosely
woven fabric that can
easily be fringed

poster board

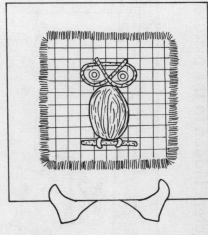

Directions:

1. Cut the material into a 6" x 6" (15 cm x 15 cm) square.

2. Start at one end and gently pull out one thread. Then do this to another side.

3. Continue doing this until the material has a little fringe on each side.

4. Glue the material to a square of poster board.

5. Glue half of a walnut shell in the middle of the material. This will make the owl's body. Be sure to leave enough room for twisted pretzel head.

6. Now glue the twisted pretzel as shown to make the head.

7. Glue o-shaped cereal inside the pretzel to make eyes.

8. Glue a stick pretzel under the walnut to make a branch.

9. Gently break a piece of cereal in half. Glue each half across the branch as shown to make feet. Set the finished picture in a little easel.

A B C D E F G H I J K L M N

O P Q R S T U V W X Y Z

This kind of cloud is made up of ice particles and looks feathery or threadlike in the air.

C I R R U S

SIGN LANGUAGE

RECYCLING Center

Recovered paper is used to make a variety of products, including copier paper, paper towels and napkins, and cardboard boxes. If you recycled one newspaper every day for a week, what is the total number of newspapers you would recycle in that week?

_____

What is the total number if you recycled one newspaper every day for three weeks?

_____

Which 2 Pictures Are Alike?

A

B

C

D

E

F

MATCHING ANTONYMS

Hint: Antonyms are words that mean the opposite of each other.

up	dry
cold	down
wet	awake
asleep	hot

WORD SEARCH

Words may be horizontal, vertical, diagonal or even backwards.

RAIN   **CLOUD**   **SUN**   **HAIL**
SNOW   **WIND**   **OZONE**   **THUNDER**

T	H	L	C	R	E	K	M	S	D
G	S	H	V	L	N	T	O	F	S
B	N	O	D	A	O	H	I	P	U
A	O	C	Z	H	R	U	O	Z	N
S	W	T	K	O	L	N	D	J	Y
Q	U	P	M	S	N	D	R	G	I
T	H	U	R	C	F	E	M	P	Z
B	A	J	H	C	N	R	K	A	R
N	I	A	R	W	I	S	A	I	L
Y	L	W	J	E	D	N	I	W	M

GRID DRAW

1. Pick a box in the grid above.

2. Go to the exact same box in the grid below and draw what you see in the box on top.

3. Keep going until you have filled in every box below with what you see above.

4. Congratulations, you're an artist!

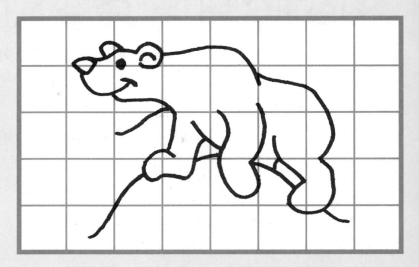

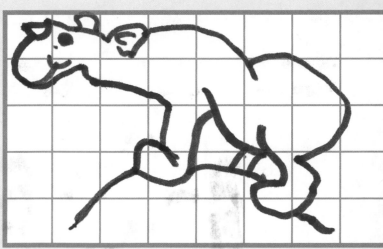

COUNTING BY TENS

Count the total number of buttons.
Hint: The buttons are shown in groups of ten.

1.

2.

3.

_10_

_30_

_58_

WHAT TIME IS IT?

Match the face of the clock to its correct time below.

1.

2.

3.

`9:00`

`3:00`

`4:00`

Make a Constellation Projector:
Preparation

Adult supervision is recommended.

Introduction to the Project

During the next 12 weeks, your child will have an opportunity to make a constellation projector that will allow him or her to project constellations indoors. Children will develop their knowledge of astronomy as they study the galaxy, stars, and constellations. They will use critical thinking skills to follow directions and understand information, and they will use small motor skills to complete the hands-on activities.

As your child begins, he or she will need assistance in gathering materials for the project. You will want to supervise or assist your child as he or she cuts cardboard and punches holes through the plastic lids.

Master Materials List

oatmeal container
  (42 oz./1.2 kg)

paper towel

black and colored
  construction paper

flashlight

glue stick

pencil

scissors

white chalk

clear adhesive tape

old newspapers

4 plastic lids that fit
  oatmeal container

pushpin

glitter or glow-in-the-dark paint

bright flashlight

crayons or markers (optional)

Constellations are pictures made by stars. To see these pictures when you look up at the sky, play "connect the dots." Imagine lines drawn between stars to form bears, lions, and other animals.

Materials

oatmeal container
  (42 oz./1.2 kg)
paper towel

Directions

1. Ask an adult to help you find the materials you need for this project.

2. Empty the oatmeal container. Wipe it out with a paper towel.

3. After dark, go outside and look at the night sky. Play "connect the dots" with the stars. What pictures do you see?

CREATIVE
WRITING AND DRAWING

SUNDAY

Pretend you are visiting another country. What country is it? What would you like to see? Write a few sentences to describe something you would see on your visit. Draw a picture of what you wrote about.

newsealand becuse
my cousins arethere.
kewibirds

MATH SYMBOLS

Math uses different symbols.

+ means plus
  (It is used to add.)

- means minus
  (It is used to subtract.)

= means equal

< means less than

> means greater than

Place the missing math symbols
  in the equations below.

1. 6 < 9

2. 5 + 9 = 14

3. 3 + 3 = 6

4. 11 - 3 = 8

5. 14 > 11

6. 7 - 6 = 1

7. 12 + 6 = 18

8. 7 < 12

9. 19 – 11 = 8

10. 2 + 2 + 1 = 5

Chapter 2: Lost

Ask an adult to help you read this story.

Hornsby and Fuzzbuzz followed the tracks.

The tracks stopped at a tall tree.

"Shh!" said Hornsby. "Listen!"

"Grrr!" said a tiny voice. "Grrr!"

Hornsby looked behind the tree.

A little lion cub looked at Hornsby with frightened eyes.

Activity 1

Skill: Antonyms

Match the words that have opposite meanings.

stop   found

little   go

lost   under

over   big

"Can you help me?" asked the cub.

"What's your name?" asked Fuzzbuzz.

"Lily," said the cub. "I lost my brother. We were playing hide and seek. I could not find him. Now I am lost, too."

"We will help you find your brother," said Hornsby.

Activity 2

Skill: Reading Comprehension

Circle the picture that shows what Hornsby and Fuzzbuzz are going to look for.

TUESDAY

Matching

Draw lines to connect the math equation to the correct answer.

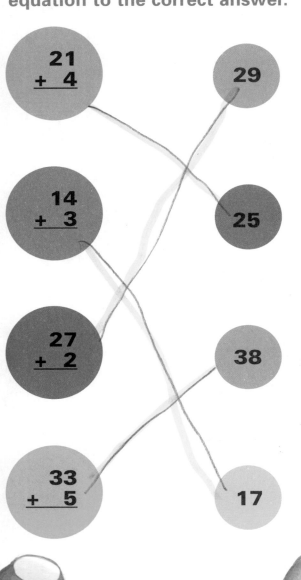

21
+ 4

29

14
+ 3

25

27
+ 2

38

33
+ 5

17

Draw the object below by copying the drawings in each numbered step on a piece of paper.

1

2

3

4

Can You Find?

Circle the characters hidden in the picture.

  Fuzzbuzz

  Birdie

 **Hornsby**

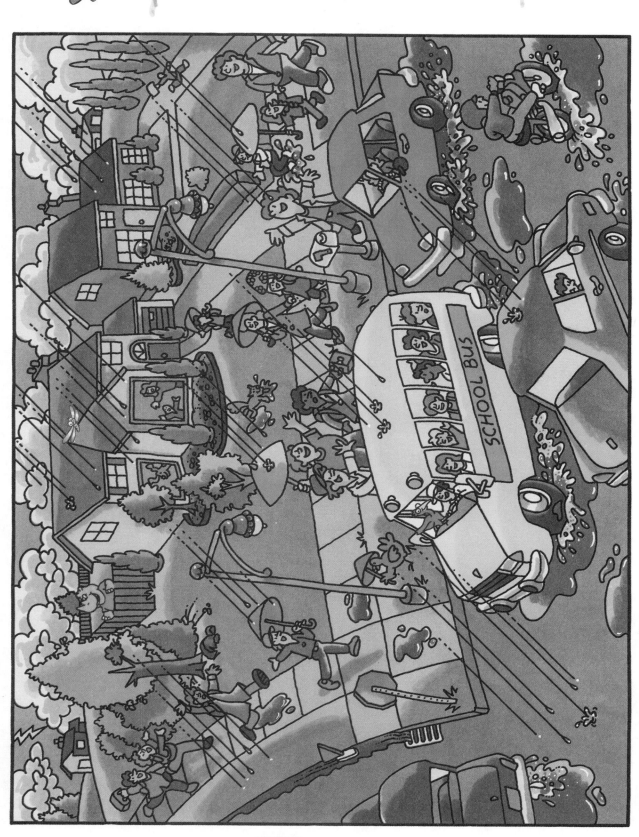

ARTS & CRAFTS

Sailboat Mosaic
Adult supervision is recommended.

Materials:

construction paper

white glue

scissors

pencil

Directions:

1. Tear a strip of dark blue paper and glue it on the bottom of a piece of light blue paper for water.

2. Cut out a sailboat hull. Glue it on the water.

3. Now pick three colors of paper that will look good for a sail.

4. Draw a large sail on one of those sheets of paper.

5. Now put all three sheets into one pile and cut out the sail.

6. Hold the three sails together and cut a zigzag across the bottom third of them.

7. Hold what is left of the sails together and cut another zigzag across them.

8. Now take one piece of each color and piece them together to make one sail with three different colors. Glue it to the picture. Draw a line connecting the sail to the hull.

9. Make two more sailboat pictures with the pieces of sail you have left.

A B C D E F G H I J K L M N

O P Q R S T U V W X Y Z

A _____ is a violent wind with speeds reaching over 300 mph. They can cause serious injury and damage.

___ ___ ___ ___ ___ ___ ___ ___
T o r N A z o

SIGN LANGUAGE

RECYCLING Center

Did you know that food and beverage containers made of glass can be reused and recycled endlessly? If your family recycled five jars every month for five months, how many total jars would your family recycle?

_____

Which 2 Pictures Are Alike?

A

B

C

D

E

F

MATCHING ANTONYMS

Hint: Antonyms are words that mean the opposite of each other.

high   white

in   closed

open   low

black   out

WORD SEARCH

Words may be horizontal, vertical, diagonal or even backwards.

~~SUNNY~~   ~~CLOUDY~~   ~~GLOOMY~~   ~~WARM~~
~~WINDY~~   ~~RAINY~~   ~~DRY~~   ~~COLD~~

S	A	F	D	I	K	R	E	G	P
Q	W	M	U	L	G	D	A	C	T
K	I	D	N	S	O	P	V	L	H
J	N	R	Z	H	K	C	I	O	B
A	D	B	S	W	I	N	R	U	T
K	W	N	W	W	S	V	G	D	J
A	S	T	E	R	A	I	N	Y	F
W	I	U	K	D	L	T	X	B	H
N	R	E	F	W	A	R	M	D	A
O	K	Y	M	O	O	L	G	H	J

GRID DRAW

1. Pick a box in the grid above.

2. Go to the exact same box in the grid below and draw what you see in the box on top.

3. Keep going until you have filled in every box below with what you see above.

4. Congratulations, you're an artist!

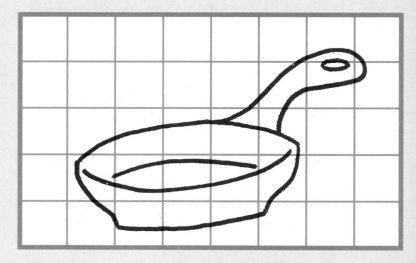

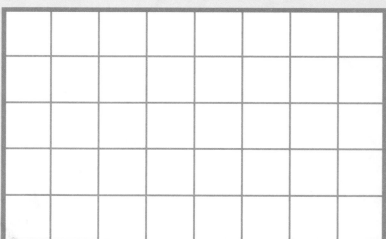

PLACE VALUES

Count the total number of objects and write the correct number in each column. The numbers zero to nine are placed in the Ones column. For numbers bigger than nine, you need to use the Tens column.

Example:

	Tens	Ones
🐝	1	2
🌼	0	9
✈	2	5
🦋	1	7

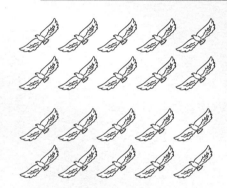

WHAT TIME IS IT?

Match the face of the clock to its correct time below.

1.

2.

3.

6:00   11:00   8:00

Make a Constellation Projector:
Measure Your Paper Cover

Adult supervision is recommended.

Materials

oatmeal container (42 oz./1.2 kg)
black construction paper
flashlight
glue stick
pencil or white chalk
scissors

A *galaxy* is a large group of stars. Our sun is one star in our galaxy. Our galaxy is called the Milky Way. You can see it on a dark night. It looks like a light strip, or line, across the sky.

Directions

1. Place a piece of black construction paper on a table.

2. Put the closed end of the oatmeal container on top of the paper. Trace around the circle with a pencil or white chalk.

3. Take away the oatmeal container, and cut out a circle a little smaller than the one you traced.

4. Place the flashlight face down on the paper. Next, draw a circle in the middle of the cut-out circle. This circle must be larger than your flashlight. Do not cut out this smaller circle until later.

5. Cover the oatmeal container with black construction paper. Make sure that the whole container is covered. (If more than one sheet of paper is needed, use the glue stick to attach the extra paper to the first sheet of paper.)

6. Take the paper off the container. Set it aside to be decorated later.

Extension

The Milky Way isn't the only galaxy in the universe. Galaxies are scattered all over the universe! Scientists classify galaxies by shape: irregular, spiral and elliptical. With an adult's help, find out about each of these types of galaxies. How are they different from each other?

CREATIVE
WRITING AND DRAWING

Your legs and feet are important parts of your body. Write a few sentences to describe what your legs and feet help you do at school, on the playground, or at home. Draw a picture of what you wrote about.

_____

_____

_____

_____

_____

_____

_____

COUNTING MONEY

Each coin is worth a different amount.

1¢　　　**5¢**　　　**10¢**　　　**25¢**

Count the coins and fill in the correct amount.

Amount	Coins
75¢	(quarter) (quarter) (quarter)
45¢	(quarter) (dime) (dime)
15 ¢	(dime) (nickel)
5 ¢	(nickel) (penny) (penny)

Jungle Tales

Chapter 3: The Know-It-All Parrot

Ask an adult to help you read this story.

"I have an idea that may help us find your brother," said Hornsby. "We can visit the wise parrot."

"She knows everything that happens in the jungle," said Fuzzbuzz.

"Where does the wise parrot live?" asked Lily.

"It's a long way from here," said Hornsby.

Activity 1

Skill: Recognize Final Consonant Sounds

Circle the picture whose name ends with the same ending sound as *walk*.

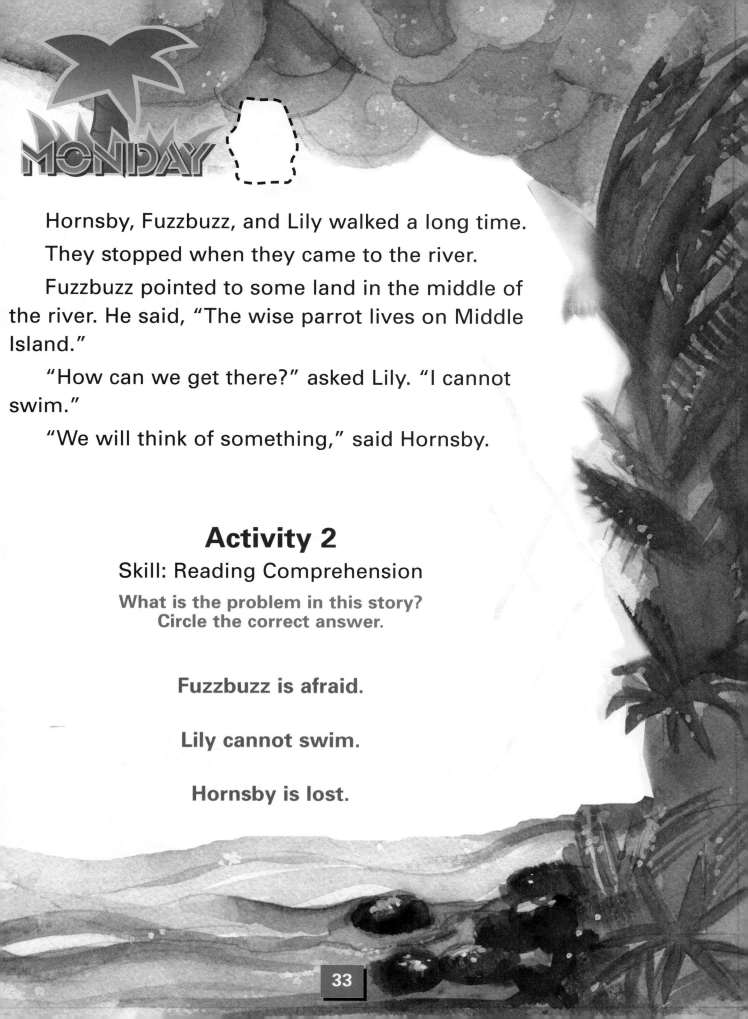

Hornsby, Fuzzbuzz, and Lily walked a long time.

They stopped when they came to the river.

Fuzzbuzz pointed to some land in the middle of the river. He said, "The wise parrot lives on Middle Island."

"How can we get there?" asked Lily. "I cannot swim."

"We will think of something," said Hornsby.

Activity 2

Skill: Reading Comprehension

**What is the problem in this story?
Circle the correct answer.**

Fuzzbuzz is afraid.

Lily cannot swim.

Hornsby is lost.

Matching

Draw lines to connect the math equation to the correct answer.

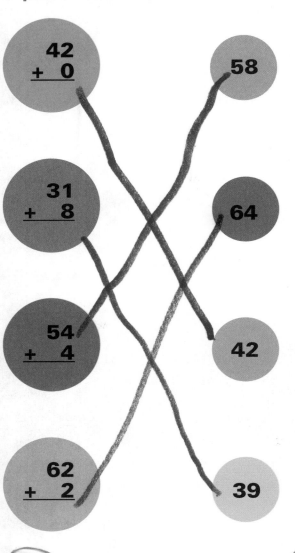

42
+ 0

58

31
+ 8

64

54
+ 4

42

62
+ 2

39

Learn to Draw

Draw the object below by copying the drawings in each numbered step on a piece of paper.

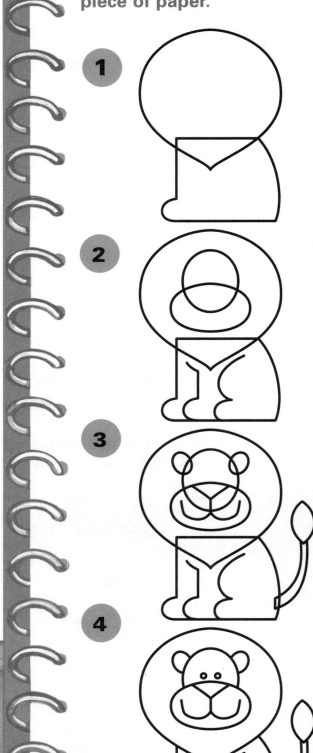

1

2

3

4

Can You Find?

Circle the characters hidden in the picture.

Fuzzbuzz

Birdie

Hornsby

ARTS & CRAFTS

Crafty Wall Planter

Adult supervision is recommended.

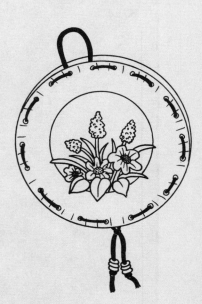

Materials:

paper or foam
  plates (2)

yarn

wooden beads

acrylic paints

paintbrush

scissors

hole punch

dried or silk flowers

Directions:

1. Cut a large circle from the center of one paper plate.

2. Put a thin strip of glue around the inside edges of the paper plates and glue them together so that the top of the plates will be on the inside. This will create a space for the flowers.

3. When the plates are dry, punch holes equally spaced around the outside edge.

4. Use paints to decorate the planter.

5. Start at the bottom. Weave yarn through the holes all the way around the planter.

6. Tie the ends together and string beads on the ends of the yarn. Tie knots in the ends of the yarn so the beads stay on.

7. Tie a piece of yarn through the top holes to form a hanger.

8. Add dried or silk flowers to the planter and hang it up.

A B C D E F G H I J K L M N

O P Q R S T U V W X Y Z

Hand movements are made possible by two muscles.
The extensors, for straightening, and the _____, for bending.

_____ _____ _____ _____ _____ _____ _____ _____

SIGN LANGUAGE

RECYCLING Center

Exhaust from cars, trucks, and factories gets in the air and makes rain clouds acidic. When these clouds release their polluted rain we call it acid rain. It doesn't sound very good and it isn't. In fact, acid rain is very harmful to plants and animals.

Name some things in your backyard that could be hurt by acid rain.

_____

_____

Which 2 Pictures Are Alike?

MATCHING ANTONYMS

Hint: Antonyms are words that mean the opposite of each other.

top   right

hard   smooth

left   bottom

rough   soft

WORD SEARCH

Words may be horizontal, vertical, diagonal or even backwards.

ELBOW	KNEE	NOSE	STOMACH
HAND	NECK	SKELETON	TOES

C	L	P	N	L	C	C	C	P	Y	K
U	S	O	E	H	E	K	Z	E	N	N
P	W	T	S	U	K	S	N	N	U	O
L	R	O	O	Q	S	B	D	E	W	T
C	D	E	N	M	N	C	P	C	E	E
N	H	S	E	L	A	S	R	M	L	L
K	A	R	K	J	H	C	J	L	E	E
M	N	E	C	K	K	S	H	M	K	K
J	D	O	R	C	H	R	O	C	S	S
J	W	O	B	L	E	S	E	L	O	O

39

GRID DRAW

1. Pick a box in the grid above.

2. Go to the exact same box in the grid below and draw what you see in the box on top.

3. Keep going until you have filled in every box below with what you see above.

4. Congratulations, you're an artist!

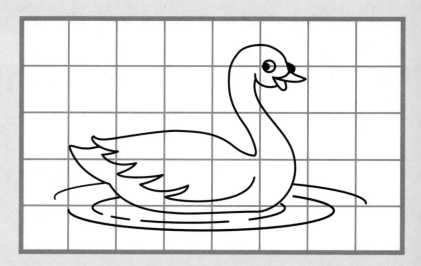

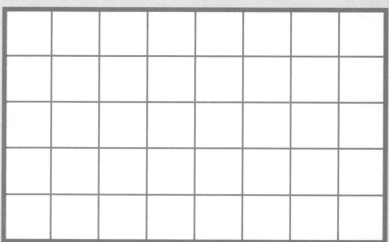

HOMONYMS

Homonyms are words that sound the same but are sometimes spelled different and mean different things. Complete the sentences below with the correct homonym.

1. Perfumes have many different _____.

scents, cents

2. The captain of the boat shouted, "Raise the _____!"

sail, sale

3. My sister ate a _____ yesterday.

pair, pear

WHAT TIME IS IT?

Match the face of the clock to its correct time below.

1.   **2.**   **3.**

5:00   1:00   2:00

Make a Constellation Projector:
Make Decorations
Adult supervision is recommended.

Materials
black and colored
  construction paper

scissors

white chalk

pencil

crayons or markers (optional)

paper cover

The sun is the closest star to Earth. It provides heat and light for Earth. The heat and light keep us warm and let us grow food. Without the sun, people could not survive.

Directions

1. Use the patterns on this page and the next as a guide for decorating your constellation projector. Cut out each pattern.

42

2. Place the patterns on colored paper. Trace around the patterns with a pencil. Then, cut out each planet, star, and comet that you make. (You can also trace the patterns on white paper and use crayons or markers to color them.)

3. Place the patterns on the black paper cover for your constellation projector. With white chalk, trace the patterns on the black paper. (You will paint these later.)

4. If you wish, draw and cut out other objects, such as other planets, to decorate your projector.

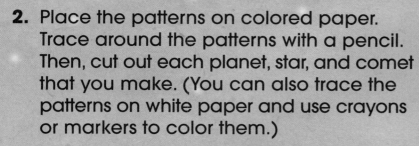

CREATIVE
WRITING AND DRAWING

There are many things that make us happy, such as ice cream, amusement parks, and animals. Write a few sentences about what makes you happy. Draw a picture of the things that make you happy.

_____

_____

_____

_____

_____

_____

_____

ADDITION & SUBTRACTION

Solve the equations below. Each answer represents a letter. Solve the puzzle by writing the letter in each box that matches the correct number. The first one has been done for you.

| 23
+ 23
46
F | 32
- 11
21
U | 6
+ 7
1E
S | 16
- 3
13
S | 20
+ 5
25
B | 11
+ 10
21
C | 10
+ 3
13
Z | 20
- 7
27
 |

| 90
+ 10
100
A | 30
- 2
28
N | 63
- 3
60
D |

| 10
+ 9
19
1H | 56
- 20
36
O | 60
+ 10
70
R | 21
+ 7
28
N | 4
+ 4
8
S | 23
+ 2
25
B | 100
- 99
1
Y |

Z=13	**D=60**	**H=19**
F=46	**O=36**	**B=25**
R=70	**A=100**	**S=8**
N=28	**Y=1**	**U=21**

Chapter 4: Ride to Middle Island

Ask an adult to help you read this story.

"I have an idea," said Hornsby. "Let's make a boat."

"But you can swim," said Fuzzbuzz. "You can swim with Lily on your back."

"Oh, yes!" said Lily.

Hornsby lay down on the ground. "Hop on," he said.

Lily got on Hornsby's back.

Activity 1

Skill: Classifying—Same/Different

Circle the picture that does not belong.

"Hold on tight!" said Hornsby.

Hornsby slid into the river and began to swim. Everything but Hornsby's back disappeared. Lily rocked to and fro. Fuzzbuzz flew next to them.

"Whoa!" cried Lily. "I am swimming!"

"Blub!" said Hornsby.

"This is much better than a boat, isn't it, Hornsby?" asked Lily.

"Blub! Blub!" said Hornsby.

Activity 2

Skill: Story Sequence

Circle the sentence that tells what happens first in the story.

Lily gets on Hornsby's back.

Hornsby and Lily swim away.

Hornsby wants to make a boat.

TUESDAY

Matching

Draw lines to connect the math equation to the correct answer.

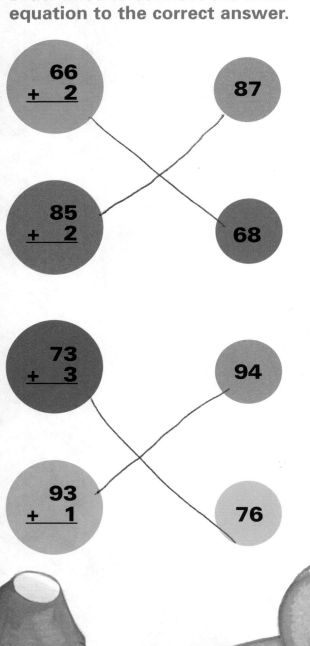

$$66 + 2$$

87

$$85 + 2$$

68

$$73 + 3$$

94

$$93 + 1$$

76

Learn to Draw

Draw the object below by copying the drawings in each numbered step on a piece of paper.

1
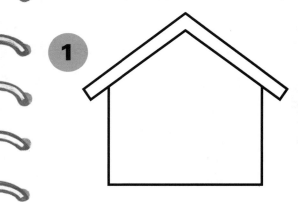

2
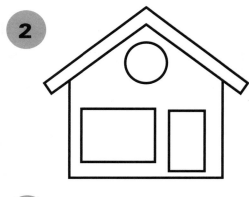

3

4

Can You Find?

Circle the characters hidden in the picture.

Fuzzbuzz

Birdie

Hornsby

ARTS & CRAFTS

Make a Face

Adult supervision is recommended.

Materials:

old magazines

white paper

scissors

white glue

pencil

Directions:

1. Cut out a large picture of a face from a magazine.

2. Now cut the face in half from top to bottom.

3. Glue half of the face to the white paper.

4. Now draw the missing half of the face. Work slowly to copy each feature so that it is as close to the picture as you can make it.

A B C D E F G H I J K L M N

O P Q R S T U V W X Y Z

In the human eye, the _____ is the part of the eye that receives light and enables you to see.

R   E   T   I   N   E

SIGN LANGUAGE

RECYCLING Center

97% of all soft drink cans are made of aluminum. If you drank one soft drink in a can every week, how many cans would you recycle if you saved all of your soft drink cans for fifteen weeks?

_____

Which 2 Pictures Are Alike?

A

B

C

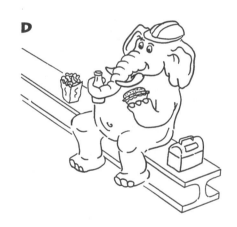
D

E

F

MATCHING ANTONYMS

Hint: Antonyms are words that mean the opposite of each other.

dark   full
happy   slow
empty   light
fast   sad

WORD SEARCH

Words may be horizontal, vertical, diagonal or even backwards.

CLAP   JUMP   LISTEN   HEAR
JOG   TASTE   SMELL   TOUCH

T	A	S	B	K	Z	P	R	A	J
M	R	U	L	I	S	T	E	N	D
E	P	H	G	T	M	I	L	Y	U
I	M	C	V	B	E	C	G	R	T
R	U	W	G	H	L	Q	F	A	O
T	J	M	C	A	L	R	J	E	G
C	A	U	P	M	K	A	S	H	R
H	O	S	F	R	S	E	M	L	L
T	D	Q	T	C	J	O	G	I	P
R	O	A	L	E	V	R	G	N	S

53

GRID DRAW

1 Pick a box in the grid above.

2 Go to the exact same box in the grid below and draw what you see in the box on top.

3 Keep going until you have filled in every box below with what you see above.

4 Congratulations, you're an artist!

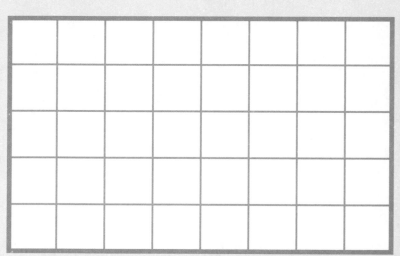

STORY PROBLEM

Read the sentence below and write it out as a math equation. Solve the equation.

If you had five pumpkins, six apples, three carrots and ten oranges, how many total items would you have?

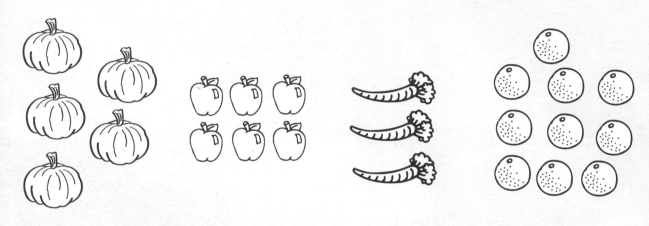

$$\underline{5} + \underline{6} + \underline{3} + \underline{10} = \underline{24}$$

WHAT TIME IS IT?

Match the face of the clock to its correct time below.

1.

`12:00`

2.

`7:00`

3.

`10:00`

Paint Your Paper Cover

Adult supervision is recommended.

Materials

old newspapers

paper cover

colored construction-paper
  cutouts

glue stick

glitter or glow-in-the-dark paint

Stars are made of burning hot gases. These gases make stars glow. A star's color depends on the heat of its gases. Stars come in red, orange, yellow, and blue. The coolest stars are red, and the hottest stars are blue. Our sun is a yellow star.

Directions

1. Cover a table with old newspapers. Place your paper cover on the newspapers. Put the cutouts from pages 42 and 43 on the paper cover. Be careful not to cover up any chalk outlines you have made.

2. Place enough glue on the back of your cutouts to make them stick to the paper. Then press the cutouts onto the paper cover.

3. Paint the chalk-outline designs from the last activity.

4. You may want to paint more designs on the paper cover. Then let the cover dry.

Extension

In the space below, use crayons or colored pencils to draw stars. Circle the coolest stars. Put boxes around the hottest stars.

CREATIVE
WRITING AND DRAWING

SUNDAY

Think of the many colors and styles of hair you have seen. Write a few sentences about someone you know with hair you like. Draw a picture of that person.

I like spilkey hair and StRate Hair

FRACTIONS

A fraction is a part of a whole. Write the correct fraction on the line under each picture. Choose from the list of answers below. (Remember, the bottom number tells you how many parts make up the circle. The top number tells how many parts of the circle are shaded.)

Example: $\frac{3}{4}$

1.
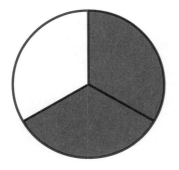

$\frac{2}{3}$

2.
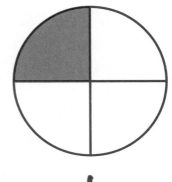

$\frac{1}{4}$

3.
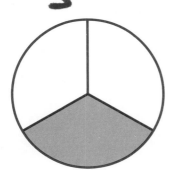

$\frac{1}{3}$

4.
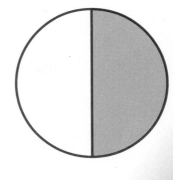

$\frac{1}{2}$

$\frac{1}{4}$ $\frac{1}{3}$ $\frac{1}{2}$ $\frac{2}{5}$ $\frac{2}{3}$

Chapter 5: Parrot Talk

Ask an adult to help you read this story.

Hornsby, Fuzzbuzz, and Lily arrived at Middle Island.

"Hell-o-o-o-o-o," said a voice in a tree.

Hornsby said, "Wise parrot, can you help Lily find her brother?"

"First, you must answer a riddle," the parrot said.

"I love riddles!" said Fuzzbuzz.

"Listen carefully. What animal always carries its house wherever it goes?" asked the parrot.

Activity 1

Skill: Story Comprehension/Draw Conclusions

Circle the word that tells how Fuzzbuzz got to Middle Island.

swam   flew   ran   walked

Hornsby thought and thought. "This is hard," he said.

"I know!" cried Fuzzbuzz. "It is a turtle. A turtle lives in its shell."

"Yes!" said the parrot. "Now go to the house of Leopold Leopard in the Sunshine Forest. He will help you."

Activity 2
Skill: Story Details

Across:

1. What do the animals need to answer?
2. The contraction can't is made of two words: can + _____.
3. What does every elephant have?

Down:

1. What animal lives on Middle Island?
2. What is the name of the lion cub?
3. Where does the parrot live?

TUESDAY

Matching

Draw lines to connect the math equation to the correct answer.

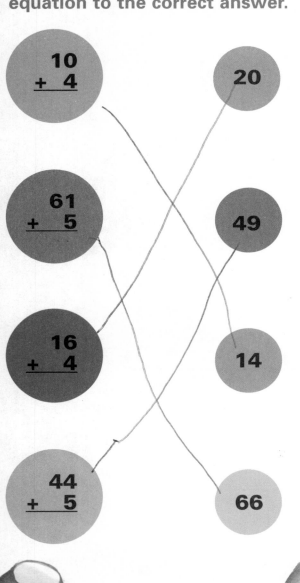

$$10 + 4$$

$$20$$

$$61 + 5$$

$$49$$

$$16 + 4$$

$$14$$

$$44 + 5$$

$$66$$

Learn to Draw

Draw the object below by copying the drawings in each numbered step on a piece of paper.

1

2

3

4

Can You Find?

Circle the characters hidden in the picture.

Fuzzbuzz

Birdie

Hornsby

ARTS & CRAFTS

WEDNESDAY

Doily Fan

Adult supervision is recommended.

Materials:

paper doilies

12" x 18"
  (30 cm x 46 cm)
  construction paper

white glue

stapler

scissors

Directions:

1. Lay the construction paper on a flat surface.

2. Glue doilies on the paper. Let them overlap for an interesting design. Be sure the edges are all glued securely. Gently rub your hand over them and press them down.

3. When the doilies are completely dry, start at the smaller end of the paper and fold it back and forth to make pleats.

4. Staple one end of the fan.

5. Snip some shapes from the folded edges before opening it.

6. Then open the fan and use it to stay cool.

A B C D E F G H I J K L M N

O P Q R S T U V W X Y Z

When surrounded by family and friends on the holidays, you feel _____.

C H E E R F U L

SIGN LANGUAGE

RECYCLING Center

Every ton (908 kg) of paper made from recycled materials saves about 17 trees. How many trees could your school save if they recycled 2 tons of paper?

_____

Which 2 Pictures Are Alike?

A

B

C

D

E

F

MATCHING ANTONYMS

Hint: Antonyms are words that mean the opposite of each other.

big   quiet

short   clean

noisy   little

dirty   tall

WORD SEARCH

Words may be horizontal, vertical, diagonal or even backwards.

SMILE   TEAR   KISS   HUG

FROWN   LAUGH   WINK   POUT

E	R	K	W	D	F	H	G	R	T
M	P	E	L	I	M	S	C	U	J
L	O	F	S	S	I	K	T	Q	H
A	U	D	R	U	T	Y	O	R	B
J	T	K	Q	V	C	E	L	I	K
P	I	X	N	G	Z	F	A	P	B
H	L	U	R	I	S	N	U	R	E
A	D	F	R	O	W	N	G	M	C
P	L	B	H	S	F	E	H	Y	L
G	S	T	F	R	W	O	K	B	P

FRIDAY GRID DRAW

1. Pick a box in the grid above.

2. Go to the exact same box in the grid below and draw what you see in the box on top.

3. Keep going until you have filled in every box below with what you see above.

4. Congratulations, you're an artist!

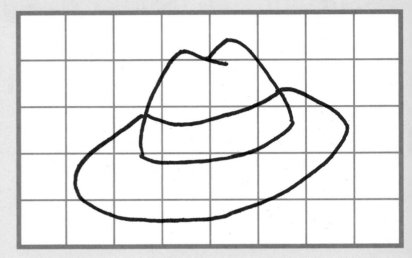

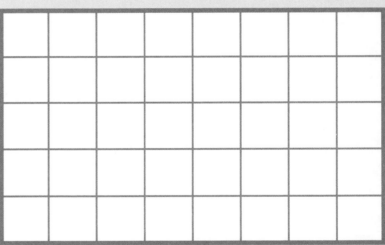

PRONOUNS

Pronouns are words that take the place of nouns. He, she, we, they, you, I and it are pronouns. Complete the sentences below with the correct pronoun.

1. My dog Randy is a male. _____ loves to go for walks.

He, (She)

2. Hornsby and Fuzzbuzz are friends. _____ are a rhinoceros and a dragonfly.

We, (They)

3. It was time for recess. I asked my teacher when _____ could go outside.

it, we

WHAT TIME IS IT?

Match the face of the clock to its correct time below.

1.

2.

3.

5:00   8:00   4:00

Make a Constellation Projector:
Attach Your Paper Cover

Adult supervision is recommended.

Materials

old newspapers
paper cover
glue stick
scissors

> Stars seem to move across the sky, but they do not. It is really Earth that moves. Other planets move through the sky, too. In fact, all nine planets *revolve*, or move, around the sun.

Directions

1. Cover a table with old newspapers.

2. Glue the circle from page 28 to the bottom of the oatmeal container. Make sure that you can still see the traced circle.

3. Place the paper cover on the table with the decorations facing down.

4. Rub the glue stick over the oatmeal container. Put glue evenly around the container so that the cover will stick.

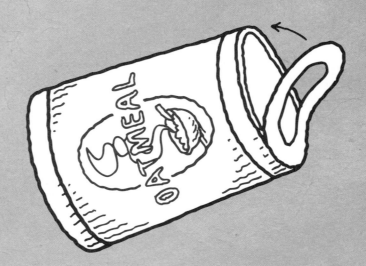

5. Rub some glue along the edges of the paper cover.

6. Place the oatmeal container on its side on top of the cover. Line up the container and the cover.

7. Wrap the paper cover around the container. Press the paper to make it stick. Let the projector dry.

Extension

Do you know the names of the nine planets? Look for the planets in a book, or ask an adult for help. Write the planet names on the lines below.

_____

_____

_____

CREATIVE
WRITING AND DRAWING

Write a few sentences about something that you might do when it is raining outside. Draw a picture of what you wrote about.

COUNTING MONEY

Each coin is worth a different amount.

1¢   **5¢**   **10¢**   **25¢**

Count the coins and fill in the correct amount.

Amount	Coins
36¢	(two quarters and a penny)
5¢	(one nickel)
3¢	(three pennies)
20¢	(two dimes)

Chapter 6: The Storm

Ask an adult to help you read this story.

When they got back to the jungle, Lily jumped down.

Hornsby looked up at the sky. "We must hurry," he said.

The sky was very dark. The wind blew.

"A storm is coming," said Fuzzbuzz.

Leaves blew off the trees. The wind roared.

"I am scared," said Lily.

"Hurry!" said Hornsby. He began to run.

Activity 1

Skill: Story Comprehension—Main Events

Circle the picture that shows what is happening in the story.

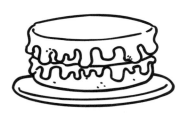

"Wait!" called Lily. "I cannot run as fast as you." Hornsby stopped. Suddenly rain poured from the sky. The wind blew even harder.

"I am getting wet!" cried Lily.

Fuzzbuzz said, "We must find a place to hide."

Hornsby wondered, "Where can we go?"

Then he heard a great crash.

Activity 2

Skill: Story Comprehension— Compare and Contrast

How is Hornsby different from Fuzzbuzz and Lily? Circle the sentence that tells how they are different.

He is big, and they are small.

He is afraid, and they are brave.

He is sad, and they are happy.

TUESDAY

Matching

Draw lines to connect the math equation to the correct answer.

22
+ 5

96

55
+ 5

27

88
+ 1

89

94
+ 2

60

Learn to Draw

Draw the object below by copying the drawings in each numbered step on a piece of paper.

1

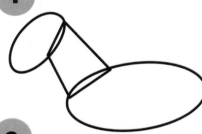

2

3

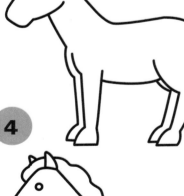

4

Can You Find?

Circle the characters hidden in the picture.

Fuzzbuzz

Birdie

Hornsby

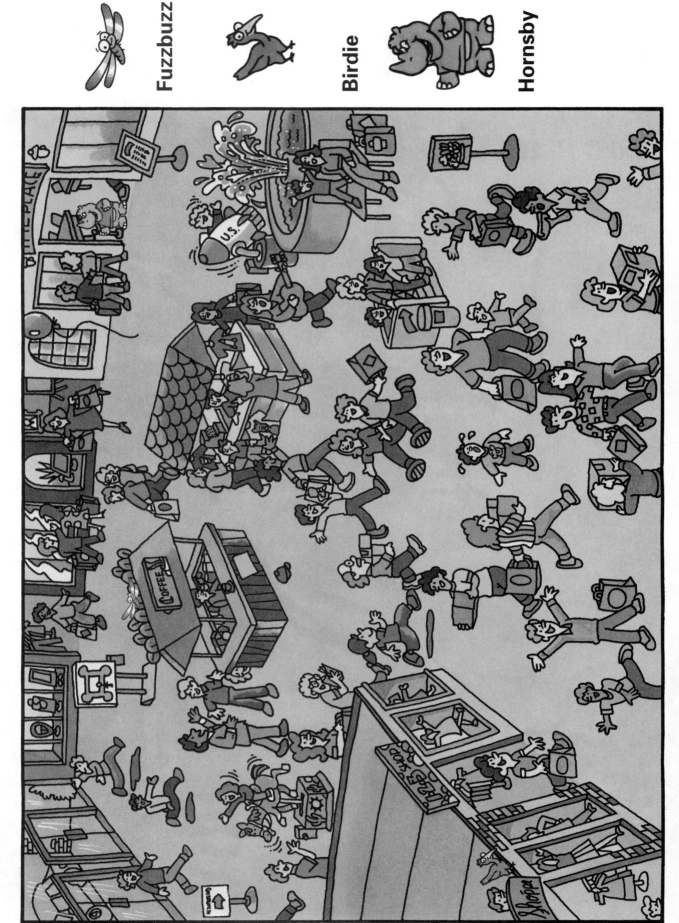

ARTS& CRAFTS

WEDNESDAY

Bird Plant Stick
Adult supervision is recommended.

Materials:

tissue paper

poster board

scissors

white glue

paper plate

pencil

markers

wooden skewer

tape

Directions:

1. Draw a bird on poster board. Be sure to give it an eye and a beak.

2. Cut it out.

3. Cut the tissue into one-inch (3 cm) squares.

4. Put some glue on a paper plate.

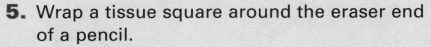

5. Wrap a tissue square around the eraser end of a pencil.

6. Dip it in glue and press it on the bird's body. Then remove the pencil, leaving the tissue on the bird.

7. Cover the whole bird in this manner. Use lots of colors or create blocks of color. Don't cover the eye or beak.

8. When the bird is dry, tape a wooden skewer to the back of it. Stick it in a potted plant.

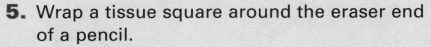

A B C D E F G H I J K L M N

O P Q R S T U V W X Y Z

You may feel this way when a friend or a pet is sick.

_ _ _ _ _ _ _

SIGN LANGUAGE

RECYCLING Center

Never dump oil or chemicals onto the ground. They can harm the land and seep into the water we drink. Dumping oil or chemicals onto the ground is an example of what? Unscramble the answer below.

O P L L U I N T G

_ _ _ _ _ _ _ _ _

Which 2 Pictures Are Alike?

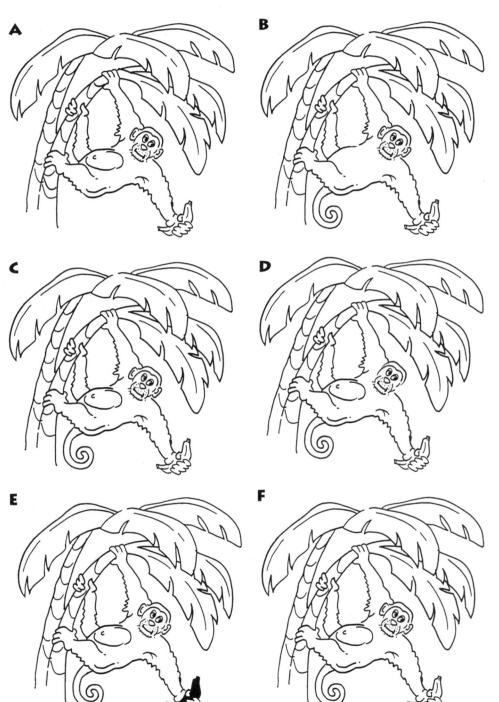

A

B

C

D

E

F

MATCHING ANTONYMS

Hint: Antonyms are words that mean the opposite of each other.

good	moving
loose	strong
still	bad
weak	tight

WORD SEARCH

Words may be horizontal, vertical, diagonal or even backwards.

KISSING   **HUGGING**   **CRYING**   **LAUGHING**
PUSHING   **SMILING**   **YELLING**   **FROWNING**

I	G	N	I	L	I	M	S	F	A
Q	A	B	D	C	H	R	W	J	H
F	S	M	T	Y	R	C	H	G	G
G	N	I	L	L	E	Y	N	O	N
N	K	H	I	N	G	I	I	T	I
I	F	U	L	A	H	V	E	N	G
S	A	M	R	G	W	K	J	A	G
S	I	P	U	S	H	I	N	G	U
I	G	A	H	G	T	G	E	D	H
K	L	G	N	I	N	W	O	R	F

81

GRID DRAW

1 Pick a box in the grid above.

2 Go to the exact same box in the grid below and draw what you see in the box on top.

3 Keep going until you have filled in every box below with what you see above.

4 Congratulations, you're an artist!

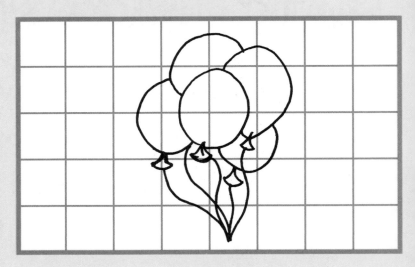

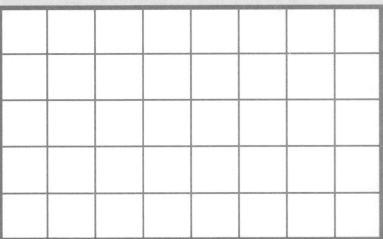

PLACE VALUES

Hornsby and Fuzzbuzz visited a big farm. They saw 125 horses, 678 chickens, 363 cows and 512 pigs.

Show how many animals they saw in the chart below. Write the correct numbers in the Hundreds, Tens and Ones columns. An example has been done for you.

	Hundreds	Tens	Ones
(horse)	1	2	5
(chicken)			
(cow)			
(pig)			

WHAT TIME IS IT?

Match the face of the clock to its correct time below.

1.

1:00

2.

2:00

3.

11:00

Make a Constellation Projector:
Cut Out Circles

Adult supervision is recommended.

Materials

4 plastic lids that fit
    oatmeal container

black construction paper

clear adhesive tape

pencil or white chalk

scissors

> Stars come in many sizes. The smallest stars are called *dwarfs.* The largest stars are called *supergiants.* Our sun is a small star, but it seems brighter than the supergiants because it is so close to Earth.

Directions

1. Place a piece of black construction paper on a table. Then, put a lid on top of the paper.

2. Use a pencil or white chalk to trace around the lid.

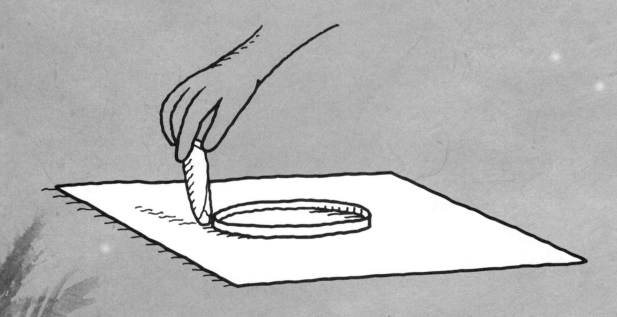

3. Cut out the circle. Be sure to cut on the inside of the traced line.

4. Place clear adhesive tape strips on the circle. Press the circle onto the lid.

5. Repeat steps 1 through 4 for each lid.

Extension

Adjectives are words used to describe people, places, and things. Find pictures of the sun in books or magazines. On the lines below, use adjectives to describe what you see.

_____

_____

_____

_____

CREATIVE
WRITING AND DRAWING

Your teacher says your class can have a special party. Everyone is excited! Write a few sentences to describe the party. Draw a picture of the party.

COLOR by NUMBERS

Add the numbers below to find the sum. Each sum represents a color. Fill in the flowers with the correct color.

$\begin{array}{r} 7 \\ + 7 \end{array}$	$\begin{array}{r} 10 \\ + 2 \end{array}$	$\begin{array}{r} 11 \\ + 6 \end{array}$	$\begin{array}{r} 0 \\ + 3 \end{array}$	$\begin{array}{r} 20 \\ + 5 \end{array}$	$\begin{array}{r} 32 \\ + 5 \end{array}$

Jungle Tales

Chapter 7: Hornsby the Protector

Ask an adult to help you read this story.

Fuzzbuzz flew close to Hornsby. "Things are falling from the sky, Hornsby!" he cried.

"Do not be silly, Fuzzbuzz," said Hornsby. "A branch of a tree fell down."

"The storm is dangerous, Hornsby," said Fuzzbuzz. "We must protect Lily."

"There is nowhere to hide," said Lily.

Activity 1

Skill: Reading Comprehension—Cause and Effect

**What made the noise in the story?
Circle the correct picture.**

Hornsby shouted, "I have an idea. I am strong. I have tough skin. You must both get under me. I will protect you."

Lily crawled under Hornsby. Fuzzbuzz flew under Hornsby.

The wind roared and the rain poured, but Hornsby stood tall and strong.

Activity 2
Skill: Adverbs

Circle the word that does *not* tell *where*.

under   there

book   beside

TUESDAY

Matching

Draw lines to connect the math equation to the correct answer.

$$13 - 1$$

$$13$$

$$15 - 2$$

$$11$$

$$15 - 4$$

$$14$$

$$17 - 3$$

$$12$$

Learn to Draw

Draw the object below by copying the drawings in each numbered step on a piece of paper.

1

2

3

4

Can You Find?

Circle the characters hidden in the picture.

 Fuzzbuzz

 Birdie

 Hornsby

ARTS & CRAFTS

Grow a Letter

Adult supervision is recommended.

WEDNESDAY

Materials:

large thin sponge

shallow plastic container
  or tray

water-based marker

2-3 packets of herb
  seeds or

small vegetable seeds
  such as:
  parsley
  watercress
  alfalfa sprouts
  radish

Directions:

1. Use the marker to draw the first letter of your last name on a sponge.

2. Have an adult help you cut out the letter.

3. Soak the letter in water and lay it in the container.

4. Shake the seeds on the letter only. Push them close together so that the seeds fill up the whole letter.

5. Put the container in a light-filled location.

6. Keep the letter damp at all times. Mist it carefully with a spray bottle filled with water.

7. In a week or so your letter will have sprouted!

A B C D E F G H I J K L M N

O P Q R S T U V W X Y Z

The _____ is the outer layer of the skin that slowly
dies off and is replaced from below.

_____

SIGN LANGUAGE

RECYCLING Center

Trees provide wood, paper and fruit. Not only
that, but they are important to our survival.
Trees release oxygen, which we need to help
us breathe. Trees can recycle themselves
because the fruits that they produce contain seeds that
grow new trees.

Name a fruit tree that produces seeds that you can plant to
grow new trees.

Which 2 Pictures Are Alike?

A

B

C

D

E

F

THURSDAY

MATCHING SYNONYMS

Hint: Synonyms are words that have the same meaning.

angry	silent
fast	cute
pretty	quick
quiet	mad

WORD SEARCH

Words may be horizontal, vertical, diagonal or even backwards.

LIFEGUARD	BEACH	CAMP	SLIDE
POOL	SAND	PARK	KITE

C	A	M	D	S	K	O	P	L	J
F	L	I	L	O	R	C	A	S	M
S	L	I	F	T	O	B	R	W	T
B	D	C	F	A	U	I	K	Q	J
E	Y	O	G	E	L	O	O	P	N
A	E	S	Z	T	G	R	V	M	D
C	K	I	T	E	M	U	H	N	A
H	M	U	A	R	P	L	A	P	K
A	K	R	X	Q	F	S	T	R	H
P	M	A	C	O	L	V	F	G	D

95

GRID DRAW

1 Pick a box in the grid above.

2 Go to the exact same box in the grid below and draw what you see in the box on top.

3 Keep going until you have filled in every box below with what you see above.

4 Congratulations, you're an artist!

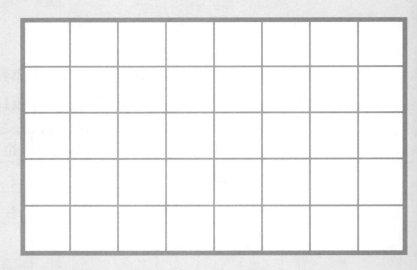

SINGULAR & PLURAL

Singular means one. Plural means more than one.
Circle singular or plural for the words and pictures below.

1. singular   plural

lions

2. singular   plural

boxes

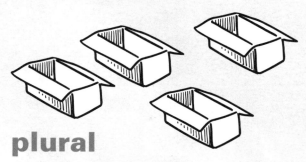

3. singular   plural

car

WHAT TIME IS IT?

Match the face of the clock to its correct time below.

1.

2.

3.

9:00

6:00

7:00

Make a Constellation Projector:
Ursa Major

Adult supervision is recommended.

Materials

1 lid with black
    construction paper

white chalk

pushpin

scissors

pencil

Watch where the sun sets in the summer. After dark, look in that direction at the night sky. Look for a giant cup with a long handle. This is called the Big Dipper. It is part of the constellation Ursa Major, or the Great Bear. The handle is the Great Bear's head and neck. The Dipper's cup is the Great Bear's back.

Directions

1. Cut out the constellation pattern below.

2. Place the pattern on the lid.

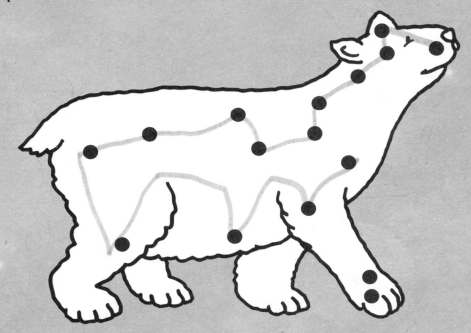

3. Ask an adult to help you use a pushpin to poke holes through the lid where the circles appear on the pattern.

4. Trace around the outline of the pattern with white chalk.

5. Push a pencil into the pushpin holes, and twist the pencil to make the holes bigger.

Extension

Find the Big Dipper in the nighttime sky. Draw a picture of it in the space below. Include other bright stars in your illustration. Ask an adult to help you find the names of these stars. Then write the names on your illustration.

CREATIVE
WRITING AND DRAWING

People have brown eyes, hazel eyes, blue eyes, green eyes and even gray eyes. What color are your eyes? Write a few sentences about yourself and draw a picture of yourself. (Be sure to color your eyes the right color.)

_____

_____

_____

_____

_____

_____

ADDITION & SUBTRACTION

Solve the equations below. Each answer represents a letter. Solve the puzzle by writing the letter in each box that matches the correct number. The first one has been done for you.

6 + 5 11	29 - 9	9 + 9	93 - 90	20 - 10	22 + 22	14 - 12	6 + 5	30 - 20	34 + 4
R									

70 - 2	57 - 54	55 - 50

27 - 22	7 + 4	66 + 2	14 + 3	1 + 9	18 - 15	99 + 1	19 - 11	40 + 10

C=44	G=17	A=68
O=10	R=11	F=100
D=5	L=8	H=20
Y=50	I=18	E=2
N=3	S=38	

Jungle Tales

Chapter 8: Hunger Pangs

Ask an adult to help you read this story.

At last the wind stopped blowing. The rain stopped pouring. The sun began to shine.

Lily said, "I am hungry. I cannot go any farther until I eat something."

"I do not have any food," said Hornsby.

Fuzzbuzz flapped his wings happily. He said, "I have an idea! We can eat honey!"

"Honey?" asked Lily. "What is honey?"

Activity 1

Skill: Vocabulary

Circle the words that you find.

rain   shine

flap   wind

honey   idea

W	I	N	D	H	F
S	P	U	K	O	L
C	R	A	I	N	A
I	X	C	H	E	P
D	S	H	O	Y	U
E	S	H	I	N	E
A	E	T	M	A	D

"Follow me!" cried Fuzzbuzz. He led them to an old tree with a large hole.

Lily crawled in. When she came out, her paws were golden with honey. "Mmmm," she said. "I love the taste of honey!"

"I think I will have some myself," said Hornsby.

Activity 2

Skill: Reading Comprehension— Character's Feelings

Draw a picture that shows how Lily felt about eating honey.

TUESDAY

Matching

Draw lines to connect the math equation to the correct answer.

27
- 6

53

33
- 1

15

19
- 4

21

58
- 5

32

Learn to Draw

Draw the object below by copying the drawings in each numbered step on a piece of paper.

1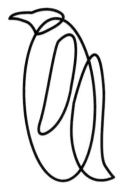

2

3

4

Can You Find?

Circle the characters hidden in the picture.

Fuzzbuzz

Birdie

Hornsby

ARTS & CRAFTS

Greeting Card Puzzle

Adult supervision is recommended.

Materials:

old greeting cards

poster board or
  thin cardboard

white glue

scissors
  paintbrush

water container

ruler

Directions:

1. Collect and save old greeting cards.

2. Cut a twelve-inch (30 cm) square from the poster board.

3. Cut out pictures from the greeting cards and glue them all over the square. Let the pictures overlap so the entire square is covered.

4. Trim off the edges.

5. Put a little white glue in a container. Add about the same amount of water and stir.

6. Brush the glue solution all over the pictures.

7. When the pictures are completely dry, turn the poster board over. Use a ruler and a pencil to draw a grid of two-inch (5 cm) squares.

8. Cut on the lines you drew.

9. Now put your puzzle back together.

A B C D E F G H I J K L M N

O P Q R S T U V W X Y Z

The long inner bone in the lower part of your leg is called your _____.

___ ___ ___ ___ ___

SIGN LANGUAGE

RECYCLING Center

Recycling of 1 aluminum can saves enough energy to run a television for 3 hours. If 3 aluminum cans were recycled for energy, how many hours would a television able to run?

_____

Which 2 Pictures Are Alike?

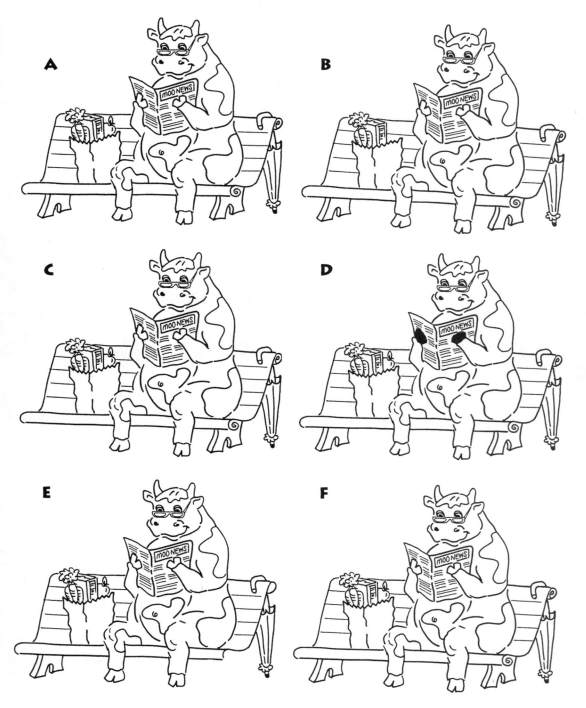

MATCHING SYNONYMS

Hint: Synonyms are words that have the same meaning.

happy	round
closed	big
circle	glad
large	shut

WORD SEARCH

Words may be horizontal, vertical, diagonal or even backwards.

BALL	FRIEND	GRASS	SWING
BIKE	FUN	SUNSHINE	VACATION

S	V	S	G	Q	D	A	P	D	C
F	U	N	O	H	S	O	G	H	D
R	N	C	Z	N	J	A	R	Q	S
I	P	W	B	A	L	L	A	D	C
E	O	A	I	H	V	H	S	K	D
N	S	C	K	O	F	O	S	S	N
D	P	V	E	N	I	V	P	W	I
W	S	H	L	A	S	A	N	I	N
F	V	A	C	A	T	I	O	N	C
S	U	N	S	H	I	N	E	G	D

FRIDAY

1. Pick a box in the grid above.

2. Go to the exact same box in the grid below and draw what you see in the box on top.

3. Keep going until you have filled in every box below with what you see above.

4. Congratulations, you're an artist!

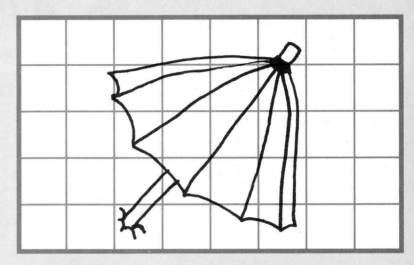

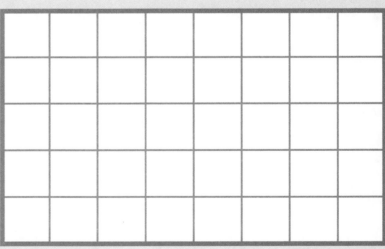

ADDITION PROBLEMS

Solve the equations below.

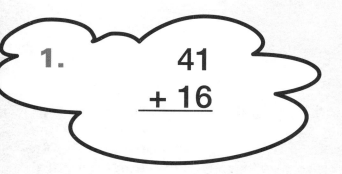

1.
```
  41
+ 16
----
```

2.
```
  32
+  4
----
```

3.
```
  11
+  8
----
```

4.
```
  17
+ 20
----
```

WHAT TIME IS IT?

Match the face of the clock to its correct time below.

1.

`10:00`

2.

`3:00`

3.

`12:00`

Make a Constellation Projector:
Leo

Adult supervision is recommended.

Materials

1 lid with black
   construction paper

white chalk

pushpin

scissors

pencil

Directions

1. Cut out the constellation pattern below.

2. Place the pattern on the lid.

3. Ask an adult to help you use a pushpin to poke holes through the lid where the circles appear on the pattern.

Find the Big Dipper in the summer night sky. Look for the stars in its cup. Follow them in a diagonal line down and to the left. You will see a backward question mark. This group of stars is part of the constellation Leo, the lion. The stars in the question mark make Leo's head and front paws. Look to the left and above the question mark. You should see a triangle of stars. These stars form Leo's back and his hind legs.

4. Trace around the outline of the pattern with white chalk.

5. Push a pencil into the pushpin holes, and twist the pencil to make the holes bigger.

Extension

Ancient people sometimes used stars to tell stories from their culture. On the lines below, write a story about Leo, the lion.

_____

_____

_____

_____

_____

_____

_____

_____

_____

_____

_____

CREATIVE
WRITING AND DRAWING

It is cold and snow is falling on the ground. You run outside to make a snowman (or snowwoman). Write a few sentences to describe your snowperson. Draw a picture of your snowperson.

_____

_____

_____

_____

_____

_____

_____

COORDINATES

Use the graph below to find where each school supply is plotted. Write down the coordinates (row number and column number) in the spaces below.

	COLUMN	ROW
crayon		
pencil		
ruler		
scissors		
eraser		
paste		

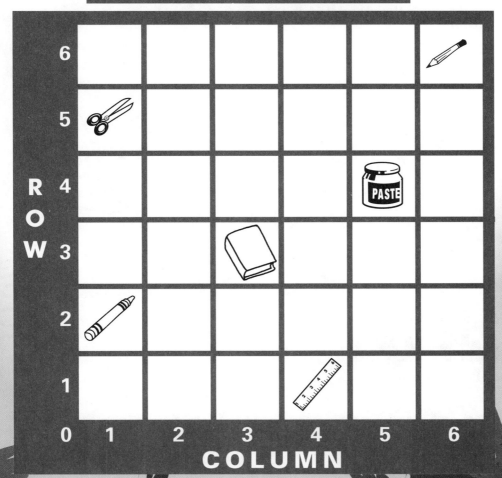

Chapter 9: Nap Time

Ask an adult to help you read this story.

After Hornsby ate a lot of honey, he yawned. "Oh, dear," he said. "I am sleepy. I must take a nap."

"Not now, Hornsby," said Fuzzbuzz. "We are so close to Leopold Leopard's house. We must keep going."

Hornsby lay down on the ground. "I just need a little nap," he said.

Activity 1

Skill: Word Analysis—Initial Consonant Sound

Circle the picture that shows a word that begins with the same beginning sound as *sack*.

"No, Hornsby! Do not lie down!" Fuzzbuzz said.

Hornsby was already asleep.

Fuzzbuzz buzzed in Hornsby's ear. He blew on Hornsby's nose. Hornsby did not move.

"What should we do, Lily?" Fuzzbuzz asked.

Lily did not answer. Lily was gone.

Activity 2

Skill: Reading Comprehension—Make Predictions

**What will Fuzzbuzz probably do next?
Circle the sentence that tells your answer.**

He will go to sleep.

He will eat honey.

He will look for Lily.

TUESDAY
Matching

Draw lines to connect the math equation to the correct answer.

48
- 44

6

77
- 71

4

83
- 81

5

68
- 63

2

Learn to Draw

Draw the object below by copying the drawings in each numbered step on a piece of paper.

Can You Find?

Circle the characters hidden in the picture.

Fuzzbuzz

Birdie

Hornsby

WEDNESDAY

Mosaic Tissue Box

Adult supervision is recommended.

Materials:

new box of tissues

acrylic paint
  (2-3 colors)

paintbrush

construction paper

white glue

water container

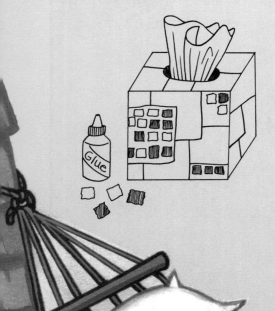

Directions:

1. Take off any wrapping paper the tissue box may have on it.

2. Paint large blocks of color all over the box.

3. Paint one side of the box at a time and then let it dry completely before you paint the next side.

4. Tear some construction paper into half-inch (1 cm) strips.

5. Now tear the strips into squares.

6. Glue the small squares in a block of color. Leave small spaces between the pieces.

7. Fill in each color block with small squares. Use different colors to make it interesting. Tear some of the squares again if you need a few smaller squares to fill in small spaces.

8. Put a little white glue in a container. Add about the same amount of water and stir.

9. Brush the glue solution all over the box. When it is dry, give the decorated tissue box to someone as a gift.

A B C D E F G H I J K L M N

O P Q R S T U V W X Y Z

Your toys were broken on purpose by a bully.
You are _____.

F _ _ _ _ _ _

SIGN LANGUAGE

Recycling is so efficient that it can take as few
as 60 days for an aluminum can to be
collected, melted down, and made into a new
can sitting on a supermarket shelf. If 30 days equals one
month, how many months does it take for an aluminum
can to be recycled all the way?

_____

Which 2 Pictures Are Alike?

A

B

C

D

E

F

MATCHING SYNONYMS

Hint: Synonyms are words that have the same meaning.

tiny	**kind**
nice	**bumpy**
rough	**jump**
leap	**small**

WORD SEARCH

Words may be horizontal, vertical, diagonal or even backwards.

SWIM   **PLAY**   **SWING**   **SKATING**
RUN   **TRAVEL**   **CAMPING**   **GRILLING**

T	C	S	L	H	J	E	S	Q	G
W	G	R	W	V	O	P	I	R	F
K	N	R	U	I	S	W	I	M	A
Y	I	S	X	N	N	L	C	B	J
R	T	V	E	U	L	G	A	H	C
U	A	M	S	I	N	P	M	Y	D
W	K	E	N	F	T	B	P	A	N
N	S	G	I	C	A	R	I	L	F
S	T	R	A	V	E	L	N	P	G
L	E	T	S	K	I	W	G	R	D

123

GRID DRAW

1 Pick a box in the grid above.

2 Go to the exact same box in the grid below and draw what you see in the box on top.

3 Keep going until you have filled in every box below with what you see above.

4 Congratulations, you're an artist!

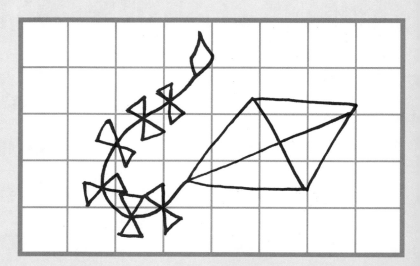

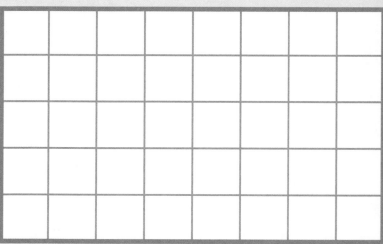

ANTONYMS

Antonyms are words that mean the opposite. Circle the antonyms for the words below.

1. black   white   red

2. high   tall   low

3. woman   man   girl

WHAT TIME IS IT?

Match the face of the clock to its correct time below.

1.   **2.**   **3.**

`11:00`   `3:00`   `1:00`

Make a Constellation Projector:
Scorpio

Adult supervision is recommended.

Materials

1 lid with black
  construction paper

white chalk

pushpin

scissors

pencil

Directions

1. Cut out the constellation pattern below.

2. Place the pattern on the lid.

3. Ask an adult to help you use a pushpin to poke holes through the lid where the circles appear on the pattern.

Look at the constellation Leo in the night sky. Then, make a quarter turn to the left. Now you are facing south. Look low in the sky to see a bright reddish star. This star is the heart of the Scorpio constellation. Scorpio means "scorpion." The scorpion's claws are above and to the right. Its back and tail look like a fishhook dropping to Earth.

4. Trace around the outline of the pattern with white chalk.

5. Push a pencil into the pushpin holes, and twist the pencil to make the holes bigger.

Extension

The "heart" of Scorpio is Antares, a brilliant red supergiant star. Antares is so red it is sometimes mistaken for Mars, the Red Planet. Draw the Scorpio constellation in the space below. Be sure to color Antares red.

CREATIVE
WRITING AND DRAWING

Place your hand firmly and flatly on the page. Carefully outline the shape of your hand with a pencil. Color in the picture of your hand. Write a few sentences to describe what your hand looks like.

_____

_____

_____

_____

_____

MATH SYMBOLS

Math uses different symbols.

+ means plus
   (It is used to add.)

- means minus
   (It is used to subtract.)

= means equal

< means less than

> means greater than

Place the missing math symbols in the equations below.

1. 12 - 6 ___ 6

2. 10 ___ 7

3. 1 ___ 3

4. 40 ___ 20 = 20

5. 19 ___ 18 = 1

6. 5 ___ 32 = 37

7. 11 ___ 15

8. 20 + 10 ___ 30

9. 12 ___ 12 = 24

10. 30 ___ 20

Chapter 10: Found Again

Ask an adult to help you read this story.

"Wake up, Hornsby!" cried Fuzzbuzz. "Lily is gone!"

Hornsby jumped up. "We must find her," he said.

"I have an idea," said Fuzzbuzz. "Follow me."

Fuzzbuzz led Hornsby back to the honey tree. There was Lily, her paws dripping with honey.

Activity 1

Skill: Reading Comprehension—Understand

Circle the word that best describes Fuzzbuzz when he woke up Hornsby.

angry   sad

worried   happy

"This is the best thing I have ever eaten," said Lily.

Hornsby laughed.

"We must go now," said Fuzzbuzz.

Lily yawned and said, "I am sleepy. I need a nap."

"Climb up on my back," said Hornsby. "I will carry you."

The three friends set off for Leopold Leopard's house.

Activity 2

Skill: Combining Sentences

Circle the word that best combines these sentences.

Lily takes a nap. She is tired.

Lily takes a nap _____ she is tired.

where   **because**   **before**

Matching

Draw lines to connect the math equation to the correct answer.

50
- 10

10

30
- 20

20

80
- 60

40

40
- 10

30

Learn to Draw

Draw the object below by copying the drawings in each numbered step on a piece of paper.

1

2

3

4

Can You Find?

Circle the characters hidden in the picture.

Fuzzbuzz

Birdie

Hornsby

Portrait Artist

Adult supervision is recommended.

With just paper, a brand new No. 2 pencil, and these easy steps, you can learn to draw a face well.

Materials:

white construction paper
No. 2 pencil
colored pencils

Directions:

1. Using the eraser, trace a large oval in the center of the paper. Leave a two-inch (5 cm) border around the tops, bottom and sides.
2. If you don't like the way your oval looks, just wipe the eraser marks away.
3. When you have the oval the way you want it, draw over the eraser marks lightly. Then wipe the eraser marks away.
4. Now use the eraser again. Draw a line across the middle of the face and a line from the top to bottom as shown.

5. Now you will be able to see where to draw the facial features.
   - Eyes are drawn on the line that goes across the face.
   - Ears are drawn on the ends of the line that goes across the face.
   - The nose goes halfway between the eyes and the bottom of the face.
   - The mouth goes between the nose and the bottom of the face.
6. Wipe away the eraser marks and erase the line for the top of the head. Draw in hair. Remember that hair covers the head and can cover your forehead too.
7. Add other features such as a neck, eyebrows, eyelashes, freckles, or glasses.
8. Use colored pencils to color and shade your portrait.

A B C D E F G H I J K L M N

O P Q R S T U V W X Y Z

You feel _____ when the teacher asks you a question and you don't know the answer.

___ ___ ___ ___ ___ ___ ___ ___ ___

SIGN LANGUAGE

RECYCLING Center

Food and beverage cans made of steel are recycled into a variety of products including new cans, bicycle frames, and even new cars. If your family recycled 2 cans a week for 10 weeks, how many total cans would be recycled?

Which 2 Pictures Are Alike?

A

B

C

D

E

F

MATCHING SYNONYMS

Hint: Synonyms are words that have the same meaning.

huge	noise
skinny	unhappy
sad	giant
sound	thin

WORD SEARCH

Words may be horizontal, vertical, diagonal or even backwards.

RAINING　　**LIGHTNING**　　**FREEZING**　　**MELTING**
SNOWING　　**FLOODING**　　**SLEETING**　　**SHINING**

S	G	N	I	N	T	H	G	I	L
F	N	R	M	E	L	T	I	N	G
L	R	G	N	I	T	E	E	L	S
O	S	E	T	H	G	J	K	N	M
O	C	B	E	U	A	N	O	K	Z
D	A	R	N	Z	G	W	H	F	D
I	P	T	S	H	I	N	I	N	G
N	Q	L	G	N	I	N	I	A	R
G	I	N	G	R	B	Y	G	E	K
G	P	C	A	S	D	E	T	O	B

137

GRID DRAW

1. Pick a box in the grid above.

2. Go to the exact same box in the grid below and draw what you see in the box on top.

3. Keep going until you have filled in every box below with what you see above.

4. Congratulations, you're an artist!

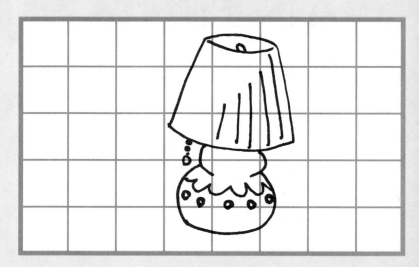

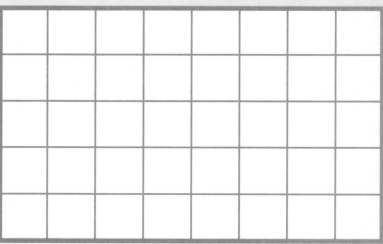

MEASUREMENT

Measuring tells you the size of something. You can use a ruler to measure inches. Take a ruler and measure each animal from left to right.

___1___ inches   ___3___ inches   ___2___ inches

WHAT TIME IS IT?

Match the face of the clock to its correct time below.

1.

2.

3.

| 4:00 | 9:00 | 8:00 |

Make a Constellation Projector:
Cygnus
Adult supervision is recommended.

Materials
1 lid with black
    construction paper

white chalk

pushpin

scissors

pencil

Find Leo in the summer night sky. Then, turn your back to Leo. You are now facing east. Look higher in the sky. Find three very bright stars in the shape of a triangle. The star on the left is the tail of Cygnus, the swan. Its wings are above and below the tail. The swan looks like it is diving into the triangle.

Directions

1. Cut out the constellation pattern below.

2. Place the pattern on the lid.

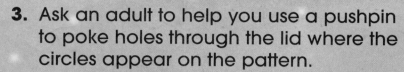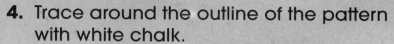

3. Ask an adult to help you use a pushpin to poke holes through the lid where the circles appear on the pattern.

4. Trace around the outline of the pattern with white chalk.

5. Push a pencil into the pushpin holes, and twist the pencil to make the holes bigger.

Extension

Depending where you live, you can see many different constellations in each season. With an adult's help, choose another constellation to use for your constellation projector. You can find other constellations in an encyclopedia or on web sites such as www.windows.ucar.edu and www.astro.wisc.edu/~dolan/constellations/ or http://starchild.gsfc.nasa.gov. Draw the pattern in the box below. Then, follow the same steps to use the pattern in your projector.

CREATIVE
WRITING AND DRAWING

Everybody feels sad once in a while. Even adults feel sad when certain things don't go their way. Think of a time when an adult close to you was sad. Write a few sentences to describe why that adult was sad. Draw a picture of how that person looked when they were sad. Include something in the picture you think would help cheer them up.

_____

_____

_____

_____

_____

_____

FRACTIONS

A fraction is a part of a whole. (Remember, the bottom number tells you how many parts make up the circle. The top number tells how many parts of the circle are shaded.)

Color in the correct number of parts in each circle to match the fraction. Example: $\frac{1}{3}$

1.

$\frac{1}{4}$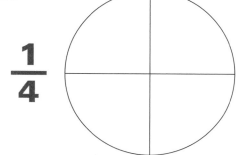

2.

$\frac{3}{4}$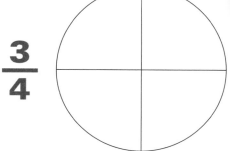

3.

$\frac{1}{2}$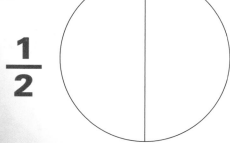

4.

$\frac{2}{3}$

Jungle Tales

Chapter 11:
Spots and Dots Everywhere

Ask an adult to help you read this story.

Hornsby and Fuzzbuzz walked for a long time. Lily slept.

Suddenly, Fuzzbuzz stopped and said, "There is Leopold Leopard's house."

Lily woke up. She looked at the house. There were spots everywhere. There were spots all over the house. There were even spots on the rocks around the house.

Activity 1

Skill: Reading Comprehension—
Recognition of Important Details

Circle the picture that shows what Leopold Leopard's house is like.

"It is beautiful!" said Lily. She smelled one of the spotted flowers.

Hornsby knocked on the door.

The door opened.

"Welcome, friends!" said Leopold Leopard. "Come in and have some polka dot cookies."

Activity 2

Skill: Reading Comprehension—Story Sequence

**Which happens *last* in this chapter?
Circle the correct answer.**

Leopold Leopard opens the door.

Lily wakes up.

Fuzzbuzz sees a house.

TUESDAY

Matching

Draw lines to connect the math equation to the correct answer.

20 − 3	23
50 − 45	5
36 − 10	17
69 − 46	26

Learn to Draw

Draw the object below by copying the drawings in each numbered step on a piece of paper.

1
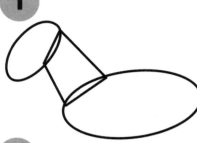

2

3

4

Can You Find?

Circle the characters hidden in the picture.

 Fuzzbuzz

 Birdie

 Hornsby

147

ARTS & CRAFTS

Sequin Fish

Adult supervision is recommended.

Materials:

thin cardboard

scissors

white glue

markers

round sequins
(extra large)

Directions:

1. Draw a fish on the cardboard.
2. Cut it out.
3. Color the fins and head.
4. Decorate the rest of the body with sequins. Start at the tail and glue on overlapping rows of extra large sequins to create scales.
5. You can use one color, many colors, or rows of different colors to make an interesting pattern.
6. Hang your beautiful fish in a special place.

A B C D E F G H I J K L M N

O P Q R S T U V W X Y Z

The world's _____ is made up of nitrogen, oxygen, argon and small traces of many other gases.

SIGN LANGUAGE

RECYCLING Center

Recycling a stack of newspapers just 3 feet high can save 1 tree. If there was a stack of newspaper stacked 9 feet high, how many trees would be saved?

_____

Which 2 Pictures Are Alike?

A

B

C

D

E

F

MATCHING SYNONYMS

Hint: Synonyms are words that have the same meaning.

street	begin
start	shining
pupil	road
bright	student

WORD SEARCH

Words may be horizontal, vertical, diagonal or even backwards.

FAT   BONEY   HAIRY   SHORT
SKINNY   BLONDE   TALL   LONG

L	O	N	T	R	C	W	P	F	H
D	N	F	S	K	I	N	N	Y	L
B	O	M	A	Y	E	V	R	E	T
L	S	R	F	T	Z	H	C	N	K
O	T	C	U	J	A	L	B	O	P
N	D	H	E	I	O	N	W	B	I
D	A	Q	R	N	I	E	F	K	B
E	T	Y	G	S	P	R	Y	G	O
K	U	C	T	A	L	L	M	D	U
J	L	A	R	J	S	H	O	R	T

151

FRIDAY

GRID DRAW

1 Pick a box in the grid above.

2 Go to the exact same box in the grid below and draw what you see in the box on top.

3 Keep going until you have filled in every box below with what you see above.

4 Congratulations, you're an artist!

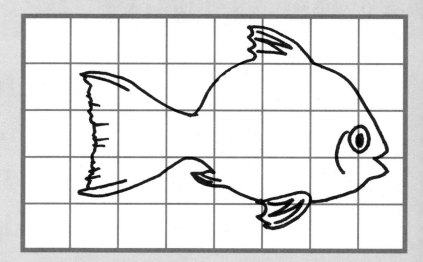

SUBTRACTION

Solve the equations below.

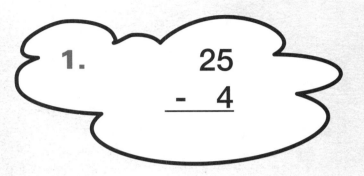

1.
$$25 - 4$$

2.
$$60 - 30$$

3.
$$12 - 8$$

4.
$$32 - 10$$

WHAT TIME IS IT?

Match the face of the clock to its correct time below.

1.

`1:00`

2.

`6:00`

3.

`12:00`

Make a Constellation Projector:
Paint Your Constellations
Adult supervision is recommended.

Materials
4 lids with constellation patterns
glitter or glow-in-the-dark paint

Directions
1. Paint the chalk outlines of the constellations.

2. Connect the holes with straight lines. You might want to add other decorations to the lids. Make sure that you do not cover your constellation holes with paint.

Shooting stars are not really stars. They are pieces of space rock called *meteors*. Meteors burn as they get close to Earth. The burning pieces make streaks across the sky.

Extension

In the space below, randomly draw about 12 dots. Imagine that these are stars in the sky. Make your own constellation by connecting the dots with lines. What pictures did you form?

CREATIVE
WRITING AND DRAWING

It is a sunny day at the park. You are enjoying the hot weather and clear skies with your friends. Write a few sentences to describe what you and your friends are doing. Draw a picture of what you wrote about.

_____

_____

_____

_____

_____

_____

Each coin is worth a different amount.

| 1¢ | 5¢ | 10¢ | 25¢ |

Count the coins and fill in the correct amount.

Amount	Coins

Jungle Tales

Chapter 12: Together at Last

Ask an adult to help you read this story.

Hornsby, Fuzzbuzz, and Lily walked into the house.

"Lily!" said a voice.

It was Lily's brother, Elmo. Mother Lion stood next to him.

Mother Lion licked Lily's fur and said, "Lily, you forgot an important rule."

"I know," said Lily. "I must always tell a grown-up where I am going. But Elmo got lost. Hornsby and Fuzzbuzz helped me find him."

Activity 1

Skill: Rhyming Words

Match the words that rhyme.

cub	mouse
house	mad
spot	rub
glad	dot

"Grrr!" said Elmo. "I was not lost. YOU were lost."

Fuzzbuzz said, "It does not matter."

"What matters," said Mother Lion, "is that we are all together again."

Leopold Leopard held out a plate. "Have another cookie," he said.

Hornsby smiled. "These cookies sure hit the spot!"

Activity 2

Skill: Reading Comprehension—
Fantasy Versus Reality

What is one way you know that this story is not real? Circle the correct answer.

A big storm happens in the story.

The animals in the story talk.

The story takes place in a jungle.

TUESDAY

Matching

Draw lines to connect the math equation to the correct answer.

48
- 24

82

93
- 11

14

37
- 23

33

75
- 42

24

Learn to Draw

Draw the object below by copying the drawings in each numbered step on a piece of paper.

1

2

3

4

Can You Find?

Circle the characters hidden in the picture.

Fuzzbuzz

Birdie

Hornsby

161

ARTS & CRAFTS

Collage Person

Adult supervision is recommended.

WEDNESDAY

Materials:

old magazines

white glue

scissors

construction paper

Directions:

1. Cut out different parts of a body and clothing from pictures of people in old magazines.

2. Assemble the body on construction paper.

3. Glue it together.

4. For more fun, make two more collage people. Hang them with string of different lengths from a hanger to make a mobile.

A B C D E F G H I J K L M N

O P Q R S T U V W X Y Z

This is often very high in the summer and very low in the winter.

_____

SIGN LANGUAGE

RECYCLING Center

Recycling a glass jar saves enough energy to light a 100 watt light bulb for 4 hours. How many hours could the 100 watt light bulb be lit if you saved two glass jars and they were recycled?

_____

Which 2 Pictures Are Alike?

A

B

C

D

E

F

MATCHING SYNONYMS

Hint: Synonyms are words that have the same meaning.

castle	rest
sleep	stinky
smelly	stream
creek	palace

WORD SEARCH

Words may be horizontal, vertical, diagonal or even backwards.

FUN	LAZY	BUSY	HOT
ACTIVE	BORING	LONG	SUNNY

D	R	K	L	Z	A	Y	M	B	S
F	Y	N	N	U	S	L	O	N	G
R	Q	M	O	G	R	H	T	Y	A
C	U	H	A	N	Y	V	P	D	H
A	Y	U	B	I	I	T	Y	R	J
R	C	S	H	R	O	S	P	W	F
Q	L	T	B	O	U	M	L	F	I
J	A	K	I	B	T	H	J	U	N
S	Z	O	R	V	F	A	Z	N	Y
H	Y	C	P	D	E	N	K	U	G

FRIDAY

GRID DRAW

1 Pick a box in the grid above.

2 Go to the exact same box in the grid below and draw what you see in the box on top.

3 Keep going until you have filled in every box below with what you see above.

4 Congratulations, you're an artist!

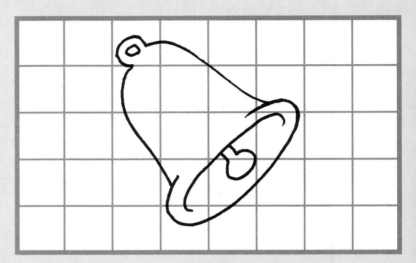

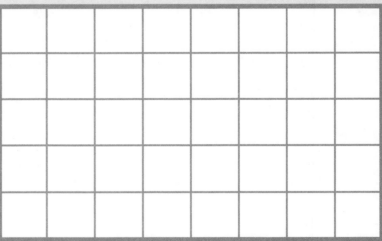

SYNONYMS

Synonyms are words that mean the same thing.
Circle the synonyms for the words below.

1. mad   happy   angry

2. pretty   beautiful   ugly

3. big   small   large

4. fast   speedy   slow

5. tired   awake   sleepy

WHAT TIME IS IT?

Match the face of the clock to its correct time below.

1.   2.   3.

5:00   7:00   2:00

Make a Constellation Projector:

Use Your Constellation Projector

Adult supervision is recommended.

Materials

scissors

bright flashlight

Directions

1. Place the projector top down on a table.

2. Ask an adult to help you cut out the flashlight circle on the bottom of the oatmeal container. This is the flashlight hole.

3. Place one of the finished lids on your projector. Go to a dark room to test your constellation projector.

4. Put the flashlight into the hole in the bottom of the projector. Turn the flashlight on, and point the projector to a wall or the ceiling. When shining the flashlight inside the projector, be sure to point the flashlight toward the sides of the projector, not directly at the constellation holes. Remember, you should never shine a flashlight on your face or eyes.

Stars can be used like maps. Sailors and other explorers used the North Star to find north. The North Star is a very bright star. It does not move in the sky, so it always tells you where north lies.

Extension

An *astronomer* is a person who studies stars. Imagine that you are an astronomer. On a separate sheet of paper, write what you would like to find out about stars.

Congratulations on finishing your constellation projector! Now, as you begin second grade, you can recognize some important constellations. You also can share some neat facts about our solar system with your class.

CREATIVE
WRITING AND DRAWING

Proud is when you're happy about something you've made or a good deed you've done. Write a few sentences about something you have done that makes you proud. Draw a picture of what you wrote about.

COLOR by NUMBERS

Subtract the numbers below to find the difference. Each answer represents a color.

Fill in the pictures below with the correct color.

30 − 15	40 − 30	22 − 11	13 − 10	8 − 4	16 − 8

Answers

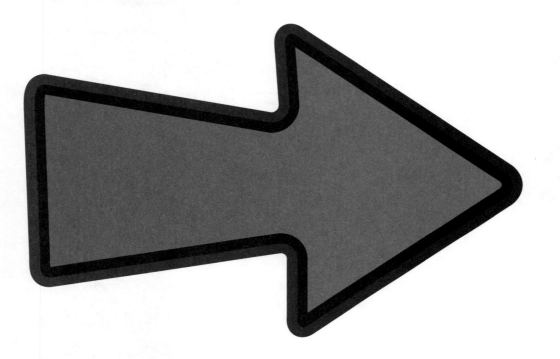

Week 1

......................➤

Story Activity 1 *Monday p.4*
Hornsby and Fuzzbuzz see paw prints.

Story Activity 2 *Monday p.5*

Tuesday p.6
Matching

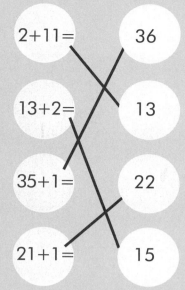

2+11=   36
13+2=   13
35+1=   22
21+1=   15

Wednesday p.9
Sign Language
CIRRUS
Recycling Center
7, 21

Thursday p.10
Which 2 Pictures Are Alike?
E and F

Can You Find? *Tuesday p.7*

Matching Antonyms *Thursday p.11*

up	down
cold	hot
wet	dry
asleep	awake

Word Search *Thursday p.11*

		C						
S				L		T		S
N	O				O	H		U
O		Z				U		N
W			O		N	D		
				N		D		
H						E		
A						R		
N	I	A	R					
L				D	N	I	W	

Week 1

continued

Friday p.13

Counting By Tens

1. 10
2. 30
3. 50

What Time Is It?

1. 3:00
2. 4:00
3. 9:00

Week 2

Story Activity 1

Monday p.18

stop   found
little   go
lost   under
over   big

Story Activity 2

Monday p.19

Can You Find?

Tuesday p.21

Sunday p.17

Symbols

1. <
2. +
3. =
4. −
5. >
6. −
7. +
8. <
9. =
10. + +

Tuesday p.20

Matching

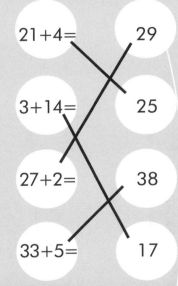

21+4=   29
3+14=   25
27+2=   38
33+5=   17

Wednesday p.23

Sign Language

TORNADO

Recycling Center

25 jars

Thursday p.24

Which 2 Pictures Are Alike?

B and E

Week 2

Continued

Thursday p.25

Friday p.27

Matching Antonyms

high	low
in	out
open	closed
black	white

Place Values

	Tens	Ones
🐝	1	2
🌼		8
🦅	2	5
🦋	1	7

Word Search

		D								
W			L					C		
I				O				L		
N					C			O		
D								U		
Y	N	N	U	S				D		
			R	A	I	N	Y			
D										
R			W	A	R	M				
	Y	M	O	O	L	G				

What Time Is It?

1. 8:00

2. 6:00

3. 11:00

Sunday p.31

Counting Money

Amount	Coins
75¢	
45¢	
15¢	
7¢	

Week 3

Lily cannot swim.

Sign Language

FLEXORS

Recycling Center

Here are some possible answers. Can you think of more?

grass, trees, birds, cats, dogs

Matching

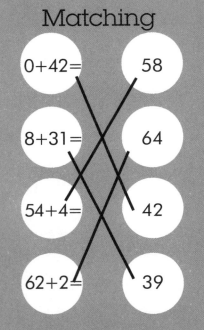

0+42=   58
8+31=   64
54+4=   42
62+2=   39

Which 2 Pictures Are Alike?

A and E

Can You Find?

Matching Antonyms

top	bottom
hard	soft
left	right
rough	smooth

Week 3

Continued

Word Search *Thursday p.39*

	S		E			K			N
		T	S				N		O
		O	O					E	T
		E	N	M					E
H		S			A				L
A				C					E
N		E	C	K			H		K
D									S
W		O	B	L	E				

Week 4

Story Activity 1 *Monday p.46*

Story Activity 2 *Monday p.47*

Hornsby wants to make a boat.

Matching *Tuesday p.48*

66+2=   87

85+2=   68

73+3=   94

93+1=   76

Homonyms *Friday p.41*

1. scents
2. sail
3. pear

What Time Is It?

1. 2:00
2. 5:00
3. 1:00

Sunday p.45

Addition & Subtraction

FUZZBUZZ
and
HORNSBY

Can You Find?

Week 4

Continued

Wednesday p.51

Sign Language

RETINA

Recycling Center

15

Thursday p.52

Which 2 Pictures Are Alike?

D and E

Thursday p.53

Word Search

			L	I	S	T	E	N	
	P				M				
	M			E	C		R		
	U		H	L			A		
T	J	C	A	L			E		
A	U	P					H		
O	S								
T		T		J	O	G			
		E							

Thursday p.53

Matching Antonyms

dark	light
happy	sad
empty	full
fast	slow

Friday p.55

Story Problem

5 + 6 + 3 + 10 = 24

What Time Is It?

1. 7:00
2. 10:00
3. 12:00

Sunday p.59

Fractions

1. $\frac{2}{3}$

2. $\frac{1}{4}$

3. $\frac{1}{3}$

4. $\frac{1}{2}$

Week 5

Monday p.60

Story Activity 1

Flew

Wednesday p.65

Sign Language

CHEERFUL

Recycling Center

34

Crossword

Monday p.61

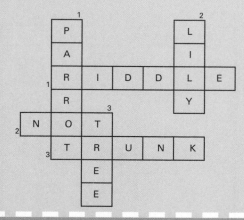

Thursday p.66

Which 2 Pictures Are Alike?

A and D

Matching

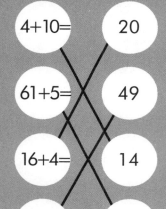

4+10=	20
61+5=	49
16+4=	14
44+5=	66

esday p.62

Thursday p.67

Matching Antonyms

big	little
short	tall
noisy	quiet
dirty	clean

Can You Find?

Tuesday p.63

Word Search

Thursday p.12

							G	
P	E	L	I	M	S		U	
O		S	S	I	K			H
U				T				
T	K				E	L		
		N				A		
			I			U	R	
	F	R	O	W	N	G		
						H		

Week 5

Continued

Friday p.69

Pronouns

1. He
2. They
3. we

What Time Is It?

1. 4:00
2. 8:00
3. 5:00

Sunday p.73

Counting Money

Amount	Coins
51¢	
5¢	
3¢	
20¢	

Week 6

Story Activity 1 Monday p.74

Story Activity 2 Monday p.75

He is big and they are small.

Tuesday p.76

Matching

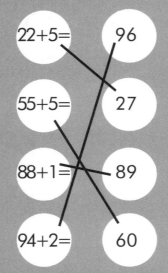

22+5=   96

55+5=   27

88+1=   89

94+2=   60

Tuesday p.77

Can You Find?

Week 6
Continued

Wednesday p.79

Sign Language
WORRIED

Recycling Center
POLLUTING

Thursday p.80

Which 2 Pictures Are Alike?
C and F

Thursday p.81

Matching Antonyms

good	bad
loose	tight
still	moving
weak	strong

Word Search

	G	N	I	L	I	M	S		
			C						
				R				G	G
G	N	I	L	L	E	Y	N		N
N						I	I		I
I					H			N	G
S				G					G
S			P	U	S	H	I	N	G	U
I			A						H
K	L	G	N	I	N	W	O	R	F

Friday p.83

Place Values

	Hundreds	Tens	Ones
	1	2	5
	6	7	8
	3	6	3
	5	1	2

What Time Is It?
1. 11:00
2. 1:00
3. 2:00

Sunday p.87

Color By Numbers

Red	= 14	Black	= 3
Pink	= 12	Green	= 25
Yellow	= 17	Orange	= 37

Week 7

Can You Find?

Matching

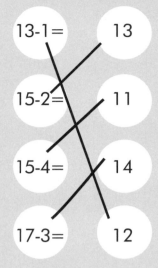

$13-1=$ 13

$15-2=$ 11

$15-4=$ 14

$17-3=$ 12

Sign Language

EPIDERMIS

Recycling Center

apple, pear, cherry, peach, orange

Which 2 Pictures Are Alike?

C and F

Thursday p.95

Word Search

				S			P		
	L		L				A		
		I					R		
B	D		F				K		
E				E	L	O	O	P	
A					G				D
C	K	I	T	E		U		N	
H						A			
						S		R	
P	M	A	C						D

Thursday p.95

Matching Synonyms

angry	mad
fast	quick
pretty	cute
quiet	silent

Friday p.97

Singular or Plural

1. Plural
2. Plural
3. Singular

What Time Is It?

1. 6:00
2. 7:00
3. 9:00

Sunday p.101

Math Symbols

RHINOCEROS
AND
DRAGONFLY

Story Activity 1 *Monday p.102*

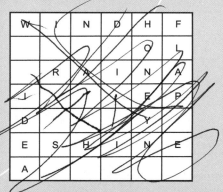

Tuesday p.104 — Matching

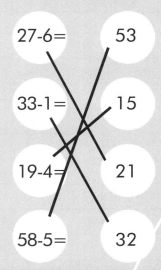

27-6 = ... 53
33-1 = ... 15
19-4 = ... 21
58-5 = ... 32

Tuesday p.105

Can You Find?

Wednesday p.107

Sign Language

TIBIA

Recycling Center

9 hours

Thursday p.109

Word Search

F	U	N				G	
R						R	
I		B	A	L	L	A	
E		I				S	
N		K				S	S
D		E					W
							I
	V	A	C	A	T	I	O	N
S	U	N	S	H	I	N	E	G

Thursday p.105

Which 2 Pictures Are Alike?

A and F

Thursday p.109

Matching Synonyms

happy	glad
closed	shut
circle	round
large	big

Friday p.111

Addition Problems

1. 41 + 16 = 57
2. 32 + 4 = 36
3. 11 + 8 = 19
4. 17 + 20 = 37

lay p.111

What Time Is It?

1. 12:00
2. 10:00
3. 3:00

Coordinates

Crayon:	1, 2
Pencil:	6, 6
Ruler:	4, 1
Scissors:	1, 5
Book:	3, 3
Paste:	5, 4

Week 9

Story Activity 1 *Monday p.116*

Story Activity 2 *Monday p.117*

He will look for Lily.

esday p.119

an You Find?

Tuesday p.118

Matching

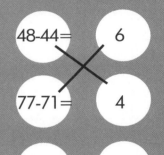

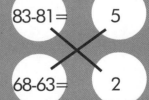

Wednesday p.121

Sign Language

FURIOUS

Recycling Center

2 months

Thursday p.123

Matching Synonyms

tiny	small
nice	kind
rough	bumpy
leap	jump

Word Search

		S							G
	G	R	W					R	
	N		U	I	S	W	I	M	
	I			N	N	L	C		
	T			L		G	A		
	A			I			M	Y	
	K		N				P	A	
	S	G					I	L	
	T	R	A	V	E	L	N	P	
								G	

Story Activity 1 *Monday p.130*

worried

Story Activity 2 *Monday p.131*

because

Thursday p.122

Which 2 Pictures Are Alike?

A and E

Friday p. 125

Antonyms

1. white
2. low
3. man

What Time Is It?

1. 3:00
2. 1:00
3. 11:00

Sunday p.129

Math Symbols

1. =	6. +
2. >	7. <
3. <	8. =
4. –	9. +
5. –	10. >

Tuesday p.132

Matching

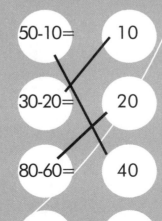

50-10=   10

30-20=   20

80-60=   40

40-10=   30

Week 10

continued

Can You Find? *Tuesday p.133*

Thursday p.137

Matching Synonyms

huge	giant
skinny	thin
sad	unhappy
sound	noise

Word Search

G	N	I	N	T	H	G	I	L
	M	E	L	T	I	N	G	
R	G	N	I	T	E	E	L	S
	E						N	
		E			O			
		Z		W				
	S	H	I	N	I	N	G	
	G	N	I	N	I	A	R	
	G				G			

Wednesday p.135

Sign Language

CONFUSED

Recycling Center

20 cans

Thursday p.136

Which 2 Pictures Are Alike?

B and F

Friday p.139

Measurement

 1 inch

 3 inches

 2 inches

What Time Is It?

1. 8:00
2. 4:00
3. 9:00

Week 10

continued

Fractions

Wednesday p.143

1.
$$\frac{1}{4}$$

2.
$$\frac{3}{4}$$

3.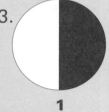
$$\frac{1}{2}$$

4.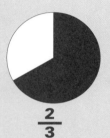
$$\frac{2}{3}$$

Week 11

Tuesday p.147

Can You Find?

Monday p.144

Story Activity 1

Monday p.145

Story Activity 2

Leopold Leopard opens the door.

Tuesday p.146

Matching

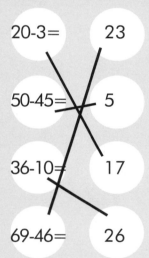

20-3=   23

50-45=   5

36-10=   17

69-46=   26

Wednesday p.149

Sign Language

ATMOSPHERE

Recycling Center

3 trees

Thursday p.150

Which 2 Pictures Are Alike?

A and C

Week 11

continued

•••••••••••••••••••••••••••➤

Thursday p.151

Matching Synonyms

street	road
start	begin
pupil	student
bright	shining

Word Search

	F	S	K	I	N	N		Y
B		A						E
L		T			H			N
O			A		L			O
N			I		O			B
D		R		N				
E		Y	G					
			T	A	L	L		
				S	H	O	R	T

Week 12

•••••••••••••••••••••••••••➤

Tuesday p.160

Story Activity 1   *Monday p.158*

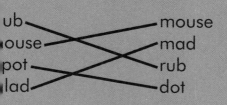

rub — mouse
mouse — mad
pot — rub
glad — dot

Story Activity 2   *Monday p.159*

The animals in the story talk.

Friday p.153

Subtraction Problems

1. 25 - 4 = 21

2. 60 - 30 = 30

3. 12 - 8 = 4

4. 32 - 10 = 22

What Time Is It?

1. 6:00
2. 12:00
3. 1:00

Sunday p.157

Counting Money

Amount	Coins
60¢	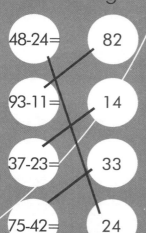
75¢	
30¢	
45¢	

Matching

48-24=	82
93-11=	14
37-23=	33
75-42=	24

Week 12
Continued

Tuesday p.161
Can You Find?

Word Search

	Y	N	N	U	S	L	O	N	G
			G						
			N						
A			I			Y			
	C		H	R		S			
	L	T		O	U			F	
	A		I	B	T			U	
	Z			V				N	
	Y				E				

Wednesday p.163
Sign Language
TEMPERATURE

Recycling Center
8 Hours

Thursday p.164
Which 2 Pictures Are Alike?
B and E

Thursday p.165
Matching Synonym

castle	palace
sleep	rest
smelly	stinky
creek	stream

Friday p.167
Synonyms
1. Angry
2. Beautiful
3. Large
4. Speedy
5. Sleepy

What Time Is It?
1. 2:00
2. 5:00
3. 7:00

Sunday p.171
Color By Numbers

Yellow	= 15	Green	
Brown	= 10	Red	
Orange	= 11	Purple	

Write Your Own Story!

Have you ever written a story? People who write stories are called authors. Use the lines below to create your own story. You can write about anything you want. The best part about being an author is it's all up to you!

_____

_____

_____

_____

_____

_____

_____

_____

_____

_____

_____

_____

_____

_____

_____

_____

_____

Draw a picture to go with your story.

Place your progress sticker next to the day of the week once you've completed the activities.

Monday	Tuesday	Wednesday	Thursday	Friday	Saturday	Sunday